Stories
of
Rome

Translated from the Hungarian by
Mark Baczoni

Alexander Lenard

Stories of Rome

Corvina

First published in Hungarian as
Római történetek by Sándor Lénárd
in 1969

Cover illustration based on Tiberis (c. 1930) by Béla Kontuly,
courtesy Kieselbach Gallery, Budapest

Cover design: Sebastian Stachowski
Layout: Judit Kállói

Published in Hungary in 2013
By Corvina Books Ltd.
1086 Budapest
Dankó utca 4-8.

For sale in Hungary only.

ISBN 978 963 13 6168 1

Translator's Introduction

Alexander Lenard is best known as the translator of *Winnie the Pooh* into Latin. That book appeared in Buenos Aires in 1958 (in an edition of one hundred copies), and this fact in itself intimates that Lenard had a far from straightforward life.

Lenard was born in Budapest in 1910, in what was then Austria-Hungary. He grew up in one of the multi-ethnic, multi-national empires that were soon to disappear from Europe in favour of the homogenous nation states that dominated our last century. Lenard chose to leave Vienna, where he had studied medicine, after the Anschluss in 1938. He went to Rome, hoping from there to sail for some quiet corner of the new world far from the madness that he – unlike many others – could see coming and wished to avoid. However, he ended up staying in Rome throughout the war, and only left for Brazil in 1952, where he became the doctor and pharmacist in the tiny village of Dona Emma. He wrote a charming memoir of his time there under the English title of *The Valley of the Latin Bear* and died in 1972.

Lenard was a true polyglot, and it is almost by chance that this book has remained un-translated into English. Lenard was a humane man with a keen sense of observation and a wry, elegiac style. There is much truth in his experience, and his humour should please an Anglophone audience. Lenard lived through many things he shouldn't have – and as he says, only a great turning of the world forces a middle-class doctor onto the streets of a foreign city, but the extraordinary thing about his writing, in many ways its finest quality, is that he never became embittered.

These, then, are his memoirs of the years 1938-1946 in Mussolini's Rome, the dying days of Italian fascism in a city rich with the overlaid traditions of three thousand years. It is a Rome that the modern visitor will almost certainly not see or feel – it is a resident's Rome, a sensitive, curious outsider's passion for the city. And it is a life – a life of the body and the mind, where music, books, food, a warm bed and a shave from time to time combine to keep a man human in the most inhuman of times. It is the story of many different kinds of people, some desperate, some on the ascendant, some waiting for a dark cloud to pass. It is a record of everyday life under fascism without the judgement of propaganda, recalling to the modern reader that even the toughest times have their routine, that one can get accustomed to anything, and that at the end of the day a man's inner world may sometimes triumph against the brutality of the external.

I have tried to retain Lenard's fluid style, which has meant maintaining a sentence structure that may at first seem odd to the Anglophone reader – however, its quality of narration, of storytelling, is part of its charm. I hope people will read and enjoy this book, which is close to my heart and often in my thoughts. Let me also say that I remain grateful to Alexander Lenard for not translating it himself.

London, 2013.   *Mark Baczoni for Klári*

Rome, 1938

In Rome, 1938

Pot-bellied popes with an eye for the marmoreal
smile down as they have from time immemorial
and trip it along the shadows of the dome.
I need something warm, a familiar face,
unmapped alleys to embrace,
and clutch me to the bosom of old Rome.

At night I lean on high Renaissance walls,
or pass the ruins of ancient rituals
creeping slow through hours of nemesis,
a hell-hound going round and round about
though sometimes as in a drought
my dry lips find a secret well to kiss.

translated by George Szirtes

Chapter I

It really doesn't matter where I begin. In this universe everything is connected to everything else. Everything is part of
that great process whose direction we can only guess at – and
everybody guesses differently. Will the great celestial machine
stop once the heat of the stars is evenly distributed in the
ether? Will Michelangelene rings of men ascend on a final
day of judgement?

Frontiers are known only to states. Events flow into one another like the waves of the ocean – and sometimes even they
seem to be serried ranks of determined soldiers, all marching
in one direction. A writer grabs reality somewhere and eventually gets to what he wants to say. He begins by saying: "Three
knights in arms are approaching the castle", or "A swallow flits
by the Doric temple"... another eight lines, we see James
clenching his fist and our hearts, somehow, are now with
James. Another page, and the colour rushes from our faces if
he wagers his fortune on a throw of the dice...

There are no frontiers between the world of books and the
living world. The history of mankind is the representation,
from a specific viewpoint, of the minor changes that come
about, occasionally, in certain proteins. A book is a mixture of
the chemical processes of the pen, paper, and printer's ink.
The rays reflected from the letters pass through the cornea
and the corpus vitreum to the proteins beyond, where they
plant the mirror image of some process already finished, and
gone. After all, we get the same adrenaline rush from reading
horror stories as we do from the experience of horror itself.
The world of books is not a world unto itself – its frontiers are
fluid – and the image of movement flows into it through ink.
Imagination does not create something new – it merely trans-
forms what has already been into a more modest, or more
perfect, form.

It would be simplest, though, for me to begin at the moment when I stepped out of the train station in Rome, with my little suitcase, and looked around the broad square jostling with people, where the trams waited one behind the other. On the other side of the square, an old Roman brick wall surveyed the scene. The people in the square occasionally shouted something in the language in which I was accustomed to hearing Don Giovanni performed at the Salzburg opera festival, but somehow it was different. In front of one door, there was a crowd of soldiers. I had last seen their uniforms, with their feathery hats, as a child: "Italian prisoners of war" the Tyroleans had laughed when they spotted a group of them. "Italian prisoners of war" I repeated unconsciously – Italians.

I was in no rush. I sat down on my suitcase in one corner of the square, and waited to see what would happen. I felt that suddenly a curtain would be drawn back, and that the play I had come here from Vienna to see would begin. Some new process would start, into which I and my little suitcase would step; we would be given a part, and would speak, and be. I waited for things to happen like they do in dreams. Someone shows you a picture, the people in it start to move, you step in and live on, while someone draws another postcard from their pocket.

The world might have turned. I spoke to a Frenchman in Venice who was well acquainted with the situation. "Mussolini has ulcers" he said, "he's ill a lot." Those ulcers could easily rupture. The wall of the stomach is four or five millimeters thick – perhaps that is all that separates us from peace. Two layers of muscle and a membrane. Ulcers grow, bleed, perforate. The operation may come too late. Funeral. Then the Army and the Party fight it out for power. Perhaps there wouldn't even be a funeral. Germany would lose her closest ally, just when the diplomatic wrangling about incorporating the Czechoslovak Germans is warming up. The tension eases. The dictatorship stops and dies. A dictatorship at rest topples, like a hoop that's lost its momentum.

Or perhaps it's Hitler's turn. It's impossible that Germany in all its wisdom and reason should not have spawned an opposition to the Idol of Köpenick. The Generals and the Workers may manage to stop this awful steel juggernaut before it reaches the precipice! Perhaps they've acted already and caught this painter-decorator on a ladder far too high for him – and the German people will keep quiet, and perhaps thank God as they do, that the Leader was shot while trying to make his getaway. Perhaps that's the news the newspaperboys are yelling, perhaps that's why they're rushing up to me! I buy a newspaper. My Italian is made up of Latin and French, but I understand this much: the dictators are still alive. It looks like I won't be on the next train back to Vienna after all. I'm going to stay here until I can emigrate to some tranquil island – somewhere under the peaceful palms of the Pacific.

And so, for the moment, here I am, and I have to start a new life.

Start a new life! Who among us has not vowed to start a new life? Perhaps after the Sunday sermon; or when the doctor tells you that your blood test is negative. Or if he tells you, "this time, you've pulled through, but be careful!". When someone starts learning a foreign language, or quits smoking... But to start a new life, as they can tell you, you need something more than that, a more painful procedure. Not even a few years of prison, or the cloister, will suffice.

If you want to start a new life, take your little suitcase and move to a foreign country. For safety's sake, you'd best not take any money, because sooner or later, you would buy your old life back with it. You'd buy your favourite books again, and music, correspond with your friends, furnish your room the way you liked it. You'll acquire a desk and a lamp like you had at home, use the same ink, take the same medicine and wait for the same flowers to bloom that you did back where you came from. Your parents' portraits will hang on the wall, your old diaries will be by your side. Your former life will emerge from these objects that accompanied you, served you well. And it will strangle your new one.

No, if you want to start a new life, you have to finish with the old one. You have to die, and be reborn. Syllable by syllable you have to learn the new language, with new words, new metaphors. You have to learn new rhymes if you want to

13

quote poetry. You have to learn that pharmacies have a different smell; the words of kindness are different here, as are the taboos. There's something new to shout when someone steps on your foot. When you're hungry, you dream of different foods – when you make some money, different numbers tell you what it's worth.

It's difficult to start a new life at the age of twenty-eight. You have roots, you've acquired some knowledge; you've got somewhere. You have capital – friends, credit from shopkeepers, a language whose every intricacy you're familiar with, which seems to describe the world you see around you perfectly. If you're a philosopher, you've developed the basis of your system. If you're a poet, you've found your voice. If you sell shoes, you have your contacts. Your wounds heal slower than they did when you were eighteen. Small sclerotic dots have formed in your arteries, the lenses in your eyes are less and less flexible. You're past your great romances, or at least you think you are; you have your habits, your favourite writers, your favourite places to walk. It's not good to start over.

It's not good when you're ten, either. At that age, it's already difficult to learn a language well enough to allow your imagination to flow free. "Before", and "a long time ago" have already acquired meaning.

Sitting there, next to the train station, I felt that there is no greater endeavour a man can embark upon than starting a new life. It's so much easier to end the old one with a bullet. You can only start a new life blindly – as if you were wandering in a fog, looking where you place each step – with the faith that with every step you take you get closer to the miracle, and you can go back to the way things used to be.

There was a little handful of my old life in Rome. The room, where one summer ten years before, I had spent a few days. The landlady had had a charming, pale daughter with deep-set eyes. It was just around the corner. I headed there now.

Chapter II

The street is still there, I remember the house. I find the flat. I ring.

My former landlady opens the door. We recognise each other, and the ten years disappear. It is indeed her! She's not changed – same hair, same mouth. She's lived in me, in some scattered neuron of my brain, for ten years, and I must say she was a quiet resident. She never bothered me, never left her room. Now, she steps out of it like Dorian Gray – she hasn't aged, or even changed. She still speaks that old, familiar language of unintelligible sounds.

I'm curious about her daughter, whom I saw from time to time in my mind's eye these last few years, and just now again in the square. Sadly, she is no more. Her place has been taken by a dumpy, short, boring woman with a downy upper lip, and I cannot hide my irritation as I extend my hand to this interloper. I carried the image of that deep-eyed angel in vain; but now see she's betrayed me.

The stone-flagged room is still there too. I lie on the bed, as if I'd come by for a liedown. "Goethe's *Cavaliersreise*, Holberg", I think. Rome is an integral part of European culture. I have money enough to last me two months here. And something's bound to come along 'til then.

In making that assumption, it turns out that I was not mistaken. The politicians – those demi-gods who direct our fate – all agreed that something was going to happen. What they could not agree on was what. Would the West mobilise if Hitler invaded Czechoslovakia? Where would Poland stand? Would she march into Teschen with the Germans? And would the Italian fleet really dare take on the British?

These great questions, when dissected into their most basic form, sounded thus: how many people would get shot in the back of the neck? How many – and who – would starve to death behind barbed wire fences? Whose children would die in the blaze? And everyone got to ask themselves: what will become of me?

There were those who did not ask themselves this question. It's so difficult to think it through to the end if you're working away, if you've gotten somewhere. If you're writing a book, you want to finish it, and avoid looking at the fire that's waiting to devour the manuscript. If you have a family, and a job, you do your work, and bring home food; and when your children eat, you are sated by their satisfaction. Your conscience is clean, so you say: come what may. I will carry on while I can.

I had nothing, and so I saw things more clearly. In fact, I had lost everything not long before. When you drop something, even if it's a bar of gold, your load gets lighter. If you have no house and no occupation, you have nothing to lose. You are free to see the oncoming catastrophe. Perhaps you even long for it, because it vindicates your indolence, and makes your condition universal.

I said to myself, if Hitler attacks, there'll be war. The French will defend themselves. Like a good European, I believe in the sanctity of the Maginot line. *Ils ne passeront pas*. Amen.

I'll stay here for a while, and then somehow find my way to France. Something's going to happen.

And then, something did happen: I fell asleep.

In the evening, I went out into the town. I knew the way, or at least suspected the path to the heart of Rome. I walked around and observed the crowds, the brightly-lit bars, the carnival of uniforms, had an ice-cream and bought a book from a vendor in the street. From this, I would learn Italian. It's nice to be able to speak Italian, and thus be able to converse leisurely, silently, with the paintings in the museums. It's so dispiriting when Titian's subjects sit and mutter at you unintelligibly in their Venetian dialect, beneath their snow-white moustaches. It's so humiliating if the only thing you can whisper to a Madonna is *"Piazza Dante"* and *"un gelato prego"*.

I'll learn Italian, and there'll be peace. Italy can't really want war. People here aren't marching up and down, agitated and screaming, like they are in Germany and Vienna. Here, they're selling the *Times* and *Le Temps* on the street! I look at these newspapers and see olive branches. Italy lacks a sense of Spartan determination – the shops are full, the faces are round, the oil and fat bubble away in the rosticcerias. No, there won't be war.

I fall asleep and wake up again. I sit down to my book.

Italian is a terribly hard language. I thought I understood its grammar – I'd read the first hundred pages of Gaspary and Otto-Sauer's language book ('The heir's goat is not blue. What does the admiral say? The conman is fiddling in the museum'). But I can't make head nor tail of my book. I sit down with my dictionary and start looking things up – I don't so much as leave my room.

"Vi aspettiamo al varco tutte 7 la dovunque me la pappo io ho gia le natiche rotte la Ceirano e sgangherata... Legiae Beiené 10,000 soldati Ailu Kebbede 10,000 Mangascia Iline 10,000 Bigerondi Latibelu Mescescia Noldie, Amadassu Burregli abissini hanno paura delle ferrite squarciate, si piglia e si va nella luna..."

I sit at my dictionary, my head swimming. Think of the Madonnas and the Titians! If I fall asleep now, they'll look at me with pity. They won't believe in me, they'll stay silent.

Irritated, I get up and go for a walk. I have to find new lodgings, because the little that I have learned tells me that these are far too expensive. I see rooms advertised for half the price of mine. I'd like to live near the post office – the post office connects me to the world I left behind.

If only I spoke Italian! But to knock on a stranger's door, a deaf-mute with an unknown language! Moving is difficult too – almost as difficult as moving to another town, and I'm settled with my current landlady. But I must move, I must make economies.

I get back to my book. I can tell that it's talking about the Abyssinian invasion, but what I'm not sure about is whether it might not actually be in Abyssinian. No, it can't be, because it says here that the author is a member of the Italian Academy of Arts. It must just be that his prose is too elegant, too clean, too neo-Dantean – maybe he uses words that are too precise, too uncommon, too evocative.

I, too, want to know uncommon and evocative words.

I sit, and sweat away. It's hot, the August day in Rome giving no quarter. My landlady is resting under a thin sheet. I feel a gratitude now that she kept the door of her room closed when she was living all those years in my memory.

But my door is open. My neighbours are shouting, but their shouting doesn't bother me – I can't understand it anyway. I don't even mind when one of them comes into my room. I think he's a commercial traveller, which is how he – too – ended up in this temporary abode. He wants to talk, but I can't understand what he's saying.

"Do you speak French?"

"A little."

We explore our common European heritage. Voltaire, Jean-Jacques…"*la situation*". He looks at my book.

"What's this?"

"I'm learning Italian."

"Are you crazy? Do you know who Marinetti is? He's a futurist! No punctuation whatever! He writes gobbledygook! There's not a man alive in Italy who knows what he's talking about. Of course he's an academician - he's mad! Don't you understand? We're living under Fascism. He'll be a minister yet. I swear to you, he'll be Minister of Defence!"

Maybe there won't be peace after all.

Chapter III

There's a room to let behind the post office. What's the name of the street, again? *Via delle Vite*, the marble plaque on the corner says. I look in my dictionary, but I'm not sure whether it's the Street of Lives, of Screws, or Vines. In any case, I go up to the third floor. The landlady is called Elsa; that's a good sign. My memory conjures up a melancholy girl with a warm smile, a brief flash of the opal she always wore around her neck for good luck. I ring the doorbell. "Camera, prendere" I practise quickly under my breath.

Elsa opens the door. *"Camera"* I say. *"Venez ici"* she replies, and I am instantly relieved. It turns out that her knowledge of French is not much more profound than this one phrase, but even this is encouraging. This room is also stone-flagged, pleasantly uncluttered, cheap. And Elsa herself does not disappoint – she must have been an extraordinarily pretty woman thirty or so years ago. I have a weakness for kings who've lost their thrones, for princes begging in rags. I like the distant glimmer of former glory. I like playing games, and one of my favourite, most intimate games is to make as if the glory of these people were not faded at all, but as fresh today as it was in their prime. I would like to tell Elsa that she doesn't look a day over eighteen, to sing the praises of her smooth, flawless cheeks. But instead of all that, I say *"trés bien"*.

Having thus become a tenant of the house, I get a lecture on the rules. There are five rooms: male tenants only, for decency. No female guests allowed.

Apart from the Capitoline Venus, I don't know any women at all in Rome, so it's not hard for me to acquiesce.

"All very respectable boys living here", Elsa explains, *"buoni ragazzi"*. There's Aldo di Naso, from Lucca, a clerk in the Ministry of Propaganda, Pietro, the shoemaker, who wants to be an opera singer, Attilio, the son of a baker in Abruzzo, who's a tenor, and last but not least, Mr Rosenwurz, a German dental technician, who's come to Rome via Sicily to get his papers in order to emigrate.

Who am I? A Hungarian doctor. How long am I staying? That depends.

Later that day, I meet the gang. They are indeed all very respectable boys. They receive me very kindly. Even if it's only to show me how much Italians like strangers, they certainly succeed. They pour me wine, hold forth on this and that, then start talking among themselves, and I lose myself on the waves of words which flow one into the next, all ending in vowels. I'm not sure I'll ever understand the string of 'o's and 'a's, but I drink it in, like a child eavesdropping on his parents' whispered secrets.

It is with sincere admiration that I observe Elsa's cat, padding to and fro around the room; it comes when you call it.

"Capisce tutto" – the boys tell me.

The only one I understand is Mr Rosenwurz, who is also happy to have found a familiar Central-European ear. I can feel his excitement at making a new acquaintance, one who has yet to hear the sad story of his life. He embarks upon it now without my asking:

"There are those who are born, there are those who are not. Of the two, being born is worse. One can be born Christian or Jewish. Of the two, Jewish is worse. A Jew can be born in Europe or in America. Of the two, Europe is worse. Within Europe, he can be born in France or in Germany. Of the two, Germany is worse. He can be born in this century, or the last. Of the two, this one is worse..." Being born in Hitler's time is the worst. Coming to Italy, waiting for your American visa... yes, his, Heinrich Rosenwurz's tribulations are the worst.

He does not trouble to translate his little speech into Italian, it's obvious that the others have already heard it. It's only the last bit that he repeats in German and Italian.

"But if I get my American visa! Gentlemen, I will treat you to a dinner the likes of which you have never seen! Champagne! Pheasant! Chicken stuffed with caviar. We'll have strawberries and cream, even in December!"

"Bravo, signor Rosenwurza" the assembled company assents.

"They're good boys" the unfortunate Heinrich tells me too. "The Italians are good people. One can live here. I'm a dentist, you know. The Italians are not good dentists. All I had to learn was 'open your mouth', 'close your mouth', 'rinse' – and I had my livelihood. It's just a shame that there's no *Gesangverein* or canary-breeders' club. I was a member in Stuttgart. Do you know Stuttgart?"

"No, unfortunately not."

"What a town! It's a lovely town! So clean and tidy! I'm from Stuttgart" he says proudly, "that is, I was born near the Swiss border..." and then adds sadly, "being born on the other side would have been better..."

And so I have a room, and don't have to worry about things for a month or so. I go and do a bit of sightseeing, like a tourist. I follow my Baedekker strictly. I'm learning.

I am introduced to the Forum. It's so small! "The ancient Romans gathered in the Forum". As if! The ancient Romans were just as busy running around after their daily bread as we are. No more than a few hundred people administered their fate while pacing these stones – just as today, our future depends on the decisions taken in the gothic benches of the

Houses of Parliament in London. So this was the site of the Senate; there's not room for too many. Here, in this temple, was kept the Treasury, and even today people speak in hushed respectful tones in the great temples of money. This is where they buried alive the Vestal virgins who had fallen into sin. They gave them a piece of bread, a jug of water, and a small lamp to illuminate their underground cell. This is where they waited, walled in, for something to happen. I sympathise completely.

Slowly, I get to know the city: I discover those peculiarities that the casual visitor never sees and the long-term resident doesn't even notice any more. I get to know the smell of the city. How different are the smells of different European cities! Budapest smells of dust, central London of malt. In Venice the stale smell of the sea invades one's room from the little channels in which the discarded lemon peel and dead cats float. The streets of Copenhagen are swept clean daily by the wind from the North Sea, leaving behind it a faint odour of herring. Constantinople, meanwhile, is the preserve of sheep, cats, and the freshness of fig trees, and Berlin has no soul and no smell at all. Rome is a mosaic: the laurels of the Forum exude pure Italy, but the smell of the river is quixotic, like a delicate perfume. St Peter's Square is enveloped by an exotic incense, while the little backstreets are dominated by parmesan and smoked ham...

I've come to know its sounds, too. The perennial bubbling of the fountains of clear water, which persevere even when all the other sounds of the street have stopped – the music of the dawn and dusk. The things the street vendors shout have come down unchanged through centuries – my ears are now no longer struck by the favourite *"stracci-cocci"* of the melon-vendors ('get 'em here'). I find a window from which every morning one can hear Liszt's arrangement of Bach's organ music. I understand the cries of the newspaper sellers, and while I can't quite understand the shouts of the children playing in the street, their sound is no longer so alien. I can even distinguish the bells of different churches.

I am friendly with the city's light as well. The morning sun seeks out the basilicas, those Greek, white marble, simple early-Christian spaces, the churches of St Saba and St Maria in Cosmedin. The afternoon light leans towards the early baroque – caressing the enormous brass rose as it peeps in through the window of the *Gesú*, and bouncing off into the cavernous blue halflight with a newly acquired coppery tinge. Or it filters through the opaque alabaster of St Peter's to touch Bernini's tabernacle. The midday sun rests its head on the exposed marble of the Forum, and the moon is most at home cradled in the arms of the gentle colonnade of the Vatican. Between the old Roman houses and in the ancient streets hangs a special, warm, yellowy light, the colour of old Rome (which fades in the newer districts). These outlying, marginalised parts of town are bare, like the outskirts of a South-American capital.

I'm introduced to Roman cooking, which has rules every bit as strict as the religious calendar. On Thursdays, it's gnocchi, Saturday tripe. On Sunday, it's refried pasta. Fridays, they eat yellow beans with rosemary and *baccalà* (the smell of which dominates Thursday evenings and Friday mornings). I learn that snails, and lentils, have their own day of the year.

I still can't speak Italian, and I sometimes get my tenses wrong, but I'm having a good time in my little room in the street of Screws, or maybe Lives. Rome is a fascinating, wonderful, eternal city; it's been through a lot. It's a good city to be in for someone who's waiting for something to happen. Years have no importance here, and I've gotten to know its lights, smells, taste. I can see it now.

Chapter IV

I pop in to Rosenwurz's room:
"Would you like to come to a concert?"
"What concert?"
"At noon, round about nowish, the crickets start chirping on the Palatine hill. They have a magnificent choir, they harmonise better than the Papal one. They've been rehearsing for a week now, and today's the big show."

"Don't joke! I haven't got time for this sort of thing!" he said, mounting the bed carefully, looking for a fly high on the wall. But the fly was familiar with the game, and is expecting Rosenwurz's move. *"Aprilabocca!"* (Apri la bocca: Open jour mouth – The most important words in a dentist's vocabulary.) Rosenwurz screams at the fly in Italian as he lunges for it, but the fly is too fast for him.

Rosenwurz descends.

"You have no idea how much trouble I have with these pestilential flies. Yesterday, it took me an hour and a half to catch the last one. And the fleas! Have you ever caught a flea?"

I had to admit I had not.

"You'll learn. Of course, it's not something that one ever has to deal with in Stuttgart. But they're everywhere here. Let me give you some advice: when you get up in the morning, stand in the middle of the room barelegged. The fleas will jump onto your legs from everywhere, and you can collect them all up neatly. If you put your trousers on straight away, you're finished."

"In other words, you're not coming?"

"This evening, we'll go to the Café Greco. My friends will be there."

Solitude is good, but only if it's of your own choosing. Good if you have lots of interesting friends, but choose your own company for an evening or a month. It's good if you cut yourself off from the world to make sense of its varicoloured images, or smooth out your emotions. But it's not good not to know anyone in a foreign city: to glance at the telephone and know that, short of a wrong number, no friendly voice will speak to you from it. I'm pleased at the thought of meeting some new people. I'm expecting something – but 'something' in life, is almost always 'someone'.

"Fine, tonight we'll go to the Greco."

"If you're going to see the crickets, take this along to read," he says, and thrusts the *Jüdische Rundschau* into my hand. "It's just come from Stuttgart."

"I don't read during music. Later."

But I won't read the *Jüdische Rundschau* later, either. It's not cheerful reading. It's less cheerful than the prison paper in

Sing-Sing, which the wardens made the convicts print for the other convicts, with a special supplement for death row. It's a paper Wailing Wall. "Family leaving for Greenland, not Shanghai, would like to exchange their tropical helmets for warm clothing". It's hard to get out anywhere but to Shanghai and Greenland. As for life in Germany, it's illegal for Jews to make music. Needless to say, it is also illegal for them to sell, or rent, their pianos. It's illegal for them to go to the cinema. It's illegal to publish a list of things that are not illegal.

That evening, Rosenwurz quizzes me:

"Well, do you think it's right, these laws they're bringing?"

"No."

He's not satisfied with my answer. He wants me to agree a little bit with the German government. Then he could explain to me nice and patiently why this or that law is wrong. As it is, he can't say anything.

I could even say that these laws are good. After all, a good law is one that serves the will of whoever's making the law, and these laws serve Goebbels' will wonderfully. They serve to create the impression among the German people that a wise and just government is acting to remove the sources of human suffering one by one. It turns out that the Jews' piano playing brought the country to wrack and ruin. So they put a stop to it. Bread will taste better when there are no more Jewish harpists in Furtwängler's orchestra. The uniformed ranks of iron-fisted, firm-jawed warriors are applying that impartial weapon, the law, in the struggle against the vile rag-merchants bent on world domination. This is a struggle of black versus white, or good versus evil; good will prevail, step by step. And the soldiers of this heroic struggle get the satisfaction of feeding those desires that the masses have not been able to satisfy since they banned public hangings a hundred years ago. Goebbels is right.

I thought the Café Greco was the café of artists and writers. Its solitary poet, however, long-haired and as dry as Don Quixote, has been squeezed into a corner by the voluble multitude. Rosenwurz knows his way to the table where the little company of which he, too, is part, is assembled. They are the 'Geographical Society'.

The trip from Nicaragua to Honduras is three hundred dollars" someone says.

"Nicaragua isn't giving visas," people reply.

"Or Honduras."

"Brazil? It's full. Who's in charge of immigration to the Aleutian Islands? The Governor of Alaska can issue visas without having to get approval from Washington."

Then the conversation falters, and starts on a new tack:

"Oh how good it was in Germany! What a miserable place this is!"

"Just listen, dear friends," an elderly gentleman says, "to what happened to me. Two months ago, I was denied leave to remain. My passport expired. I've no money. I've had a letter from the police telling me to leave. And what have they done about it? Nothing. I'm still here, and I've not seen hide nor hair of a policeman. They're just leaving me to it."

"Unheard of! This sort of thing would never happen in Germany!"

I imagine it would be more stimulating to go and talk to the poet. Rosenwurz told me about him on the way here: the dry old Don is none other than Lewis – the Irish author of "The Rose that Never Dies". Since when, which is to say for the last twenty years, he's been resting at the Greco, among the gentle spirits of former guests like Goethe, Schopenhauer, Morse, Buffalo Bill, Gogol, and D'Annunzio. It's easy to be great among the greats.

The Irish poet greets me loftily. New patrons of the café usually treat him to a glass of milk and a pastry; in return, he introduces them to the old regulars. That's how it works in the Café Greco. This is also, in fact, how the author of "The Rose that Never Dies" makes his living, and it is on the arm of the exalted bard that the newly-arrived stranger is introduced into the sanctum of the Roman Olympus.

"Hungary? Oh!"

And he takes me straight to the Hungarian table, I could almost say the Hungarian colony. At the time, I was unaware that Lewis' stock of adjectives stretched only to one, and was therefore a little touched when he introduced me by saying:

"I present you a great Hungarian!"

My fellow-countrymen introduce themselves, we shake hands. They are almost all doctors. Dentists, GPs, medical students. They were a little hesitant.

I understood for the first time what Fascism means in Italy. It's not the same murderous machinery as Hitler's, but it creates mistrust. If everyone could say what they think, their dictatorship would collapse. In order to silence people, they must sow mistrust. They need policemen who grab you and drag you off mid-sentence. If people think even their friends could be policemen, they'll stay silent.

We feel each other out with coded phrases. Then I can feel that they're testing me. They want to establish, if nothing else, whether I'm really a doctor. The questions come one after another, as if it were pre-arranged:

"I wonder if you happen to recall what those funny little growths on the heart are called that some mentally challenged people have…"

"The formula for Prontosil…"

"The symptoms of atropine poisoning…"

I can see that I've managed to reassure them. They get back to the topic at hand. This is a "geographical society" too. The problem here is the same: how can one get away in time from war, from Fascism, from the new religion: racial hatred? Which is the country where free men are still wanted (even if they have to become ice cream vendors)?

Brazil? They want a certificate of racial purity. After all, they have to protect the bloodlines of the indigenous Indians, and they've already started putting up statues of Hitler.

"Won't the Hungarian consulate give you a certificate?"

The assembled company laughs. "The Consulate is the fiefdom of the Director, vitéz Rühössy. He's a Saxon, and his original name was Reuter, but they say he's a personal friend of Horthy's. There's no way he'll hand out the certificates. He won't help undesirable elements emigrate. He's looking after the Brazilian national interest. He won't even extend passports. But the Ladies of Malta get their papers all right!"

"Who're they?"

The company laughs again. "They're the young ladies who represent our fair home in Malta, three months at a time.

Then they have to spend three months away from the island, and this enforced exile is spent in Rome. Here, their passports are extended and the necessary permits obtained, by his excellency councillor Rákos, who acts in their interest. Then they can go back to their duty station; their movements are followed with keen interest by the British Mediterranean Fleet. The British Admirals know them as well as they know the deck of their first command. They don't come to the Greco – their main camp is at the Café Aragno.

"Nicaragua?" I ask.

"You need thirty thousand dollars."

"Honduras?"

"Twenty five."

"Here's Sommer!" one of them, who had introduced himself as a dentist, shouts. "We'll see how he got on with the Consul from Paraguay."

Sommer is a dentist too. He's got a good practice, but he's scared. He's determined to leave. He even wrote to Queen Geraldine in Albania, but her Royal Highness, or so she said, could only put him on the waiting list for the moment. Sommer is, thus, first of the European dentists who don't want to die on the list at the Albanian ministry of the interior (or possibly exterior); but he won't rest.

"What did the Paraguayan Consul say?"

Sommer waves his hand dismissively. "I had a better idea."

"Let's hear it!"

"I've written to the Dalai Lama. It's a sure bet. Tibet is empty, all plains. There's room for us all. There's nothing better than sitting up there in those majestic heights, drinking your yak-milk tea. There's not a single dentist in the place. If the Dalai Lama gives us immigration permits, the Maharajah of Nepal won't refuse us transit visas."

Transit visas are not a problem.

"What language did you write to him in?" I ask.

"Chinese, of course. Tibet is officially a protectorate of China. And the world of pictograms extends all the way from the Pacific Ocean to Turkestan. The Dalai Lama understands a classical letter from the Han dynasty in exactly the same way the Pope would understand it if it were in Latin."

"But who wrote the letter?"

"The Chinese priest who lives near me, in the college of the Propaganda Fide. You don't believe me? Here, I've brought you a copy. I wrote it in all our names."

He takes it out. Even on the copy, the painstaking brush-strokes are visible. There are five rows of mysterious characters; and they will carry the hopes of this entire table far away, across the Himalayas. Runciman is negotiating in Prague, Skoda and Krupp are casting steel, there's martial music on the radio, the Jüdische Rundschau laments, the Poles are practising their air-defense, the Italian papers are belittling the Czechoslovak patchwork-state – perhaps, after all, the reincarnated God of Lhasa can grant a handful of people a little peace. His blessings may extend to visas. Sommer and friends could follow in Kőrösi Csoma's footsteps to Darjeeling, towards the Himalayas, far, far away from Rühössy…

Sommer accompanies me part of the way home.

"Tibet's a good plan," I say.

Sommer looks me very seriously in the eye.

"Don't take me for a fool," he tells me calmly. "It's just our little game. Sometimes, you have to play these little games, otherwise you'll go mad."

"But the letter, your letter in Chinese!"

"That! This afternoon, I took a brush and copied out the label on my five-pound bag of tea. It's a tea advert! My dear sir, it's impossible to get into Tibet too. Anyhow, I hope you have a pleasant stay in Rome. Goodnight."

Chapter V

The next day, Rosenwurz catches me:

"It's a shame you went over to the other table last night. There was a lot more useful information to be had. Look," he says, taking a newspaper clipping out of his pocket, "Bill Webb, an American Senator says that they should let 10,000 European political exiles into America. They'll let us immigrate! I'll have my visa!" Then he adds, "And our dinner.

We'll go somewhere good, a first-rate place, you'll see. We'll have our fill!"

Then Attilio takes over. He's a touchingly nice young man. He's a passionate teacher. He is aware of, and enjoys, his superiority. He discovers the Berlitz method all by himself. He jumps: *io salto*. He runs: *corro*. He does energetic athletic stretches until the sweat shows on his forehead: *sudo*. He collapses, exhausted, onto the bed: *sono stanco*.

Learning a language is a good and pleasant occupation. Changing languages is a jarring experience, though. Only numbers, colours, and animals survive the transition. Concepts and tenses change. Our favourite expressions, the little linguistic peculiarities by which our friends recognise us, disappear. Our clever jokes lose their meaning. Our wise expressions become comic or banal. A simple man will get his full vocabulary back relatively quickly, once he's managed to master the grammar, but woe betide the man who has to relearn all the words from prep school, secondary school and university! He suddenly realises just how many ideas go into making up a world, the boundlessness of the one he's lost, and how hopeless is his campaign to conquer this new one. It's a tragedy that language encompasses all the world, while nations have borders – it's why some nations are so obsessed with conquest. One can conquer by learning – as I am trying to conquer Italy now, or by instruction – by drumming their language into other people's heads. If only people realised that it was easier to learn.

Attilio is a good teacher: he knows that language, ideas, and everyday life are to be found all together reflected in the same neurons, rooted in the same pathways of our brains. He takes me out into the city. Not into the Papal and regal city of my aged Baedeker, that artistic dream of times already past, not into the symbolism of the new Italian 'Imperio' – he takes me into the city that lives alongside these other two, and that will outlive them both. He shows me how to drink from the roadside fountains: you block the bottom of the metal spout with your hand, and the refreshing, clean water arcs into your mouth from the little hole in the top. He shows me that here, it's the baker who sells herbs, and the grocer who sells meat.

It's as if anatomy itself were different here: they have different cuts of beef (I learn the names of the cuts), I can't recognise them at all. They leave the leg steaks on the bone, which makes them look like the models from my topographic anatomy course. I learn that if the shutters of a house are held closed with a chain, that means it's a brothel, and that these historic establishments are open day and night. I learn – and this is the most important thing I learn – what a secret policeman is, and how to recognise one.

The sort of police who look for your stolen wristwatch, or try to solve grisly murders, play absolutely no role in a Fascist state. The police are the guardians of the state. They serve to defend the institution against which, and without which – according to Fascist dogma – nothing can happen. The police serve to protect the state from its most dangerous enemies: its citizens. The secret policeman stands on the street and, as Attilio points out to me, marks the route of the Duce. From the balcony of the Palazzo Venezia, photographed a thousand times a day, to the Villa Torlonia, there's one every ten meters. They are all around the Palazzo Venezia. They're in serried ranks near Trajan's Forum. They are the first signs that you're entering the vicinity of the Foreign Ministry and the Ministry of Defence. The law-abiding citizen prefers to avoid these areas, and if they nonetheless have to go to the Duce's palace, they walk in a straight line and never stop. They wouldn't dream of walking that way with any sort of package. They'd get stopped by a secret policeman: "Papers, please." He'd drag them into a doorway. "Where are you going? Why? Who are you going to meet? Are you a Party member? Why? Why not?" It can easily turn into a two or three day interrogation at the police station, and if you happen to be entirely innocent, you'll be lucky to get away with the advice that in future you should watch where you're going. But it can also happen that – just to be safe – they intern you for a year or two in some Godforsaken little village. Just then, the case of a Brazilian man was the talk of the entire town: they had caught him in front of the Duce's villa with camera in hand. He said he wanted a photo of the famous politician. That night, they arrested all the Brazilians in Rome, and it was only the inter-

30

vention of the Brazilian ambassador that helped smooth the incident over.

Attilio explains how I can recognise a secret policeman: they're between twenty and thirty (after that, they're assigned a desk-job). They are, to a man, Neapolitan or Sicilian. They usually have a newspaper in their pocket. From time to time, they would be issued with umbrellas, or green ties, or tan mackintoshes – which became a sort of uniform. They each have their own patch – they can spend years standing in the same spot, eight hours a day. Their role is harder than a straightforward sentry's, for they have to pretend that they're just simple, quiet, idle young men waiting for some girl, or just standing around with nothing to do. But all that standing around has given rise to certain movements that make them look like the Venus Vulgivagus – the same bend of the knee, the same odd smile now and then. The word 'secret' is thus misleading. They are no more secret policemen than His Highness's true Privy Councillors were truly private. I learn my lesson, and Attilio gives me my final exam: yes, he's one. No, not him. It reminds me of Italian opera, where one of the characters will stand plum centre stage and sing "no one can see me here, no-one knows me." The Italians are conservative, and masters of the art of illusion.

In that sense, the secret policemen are the true representatives of the Italian people: they are the ones who lend Italian society the illusion of enthusiasm. If the Duce visits some provincial town, they're there a day ahead of him. They applaud him at the station, they acclaim him under the inevitable balcony. If the Duce goes down into a mine (for a photo opportunity in a mining helmet – the Duce as foremost miner of the Imperium), they are the miners. If he visits a harvest (the Imperium's foremost harvester), they are the peasants. They are the adoring seamen – and mean-spirited rumour would have it that the little old lady who bends to kiss the Duce's hand and present him with a petition is, in fact, a seargant-major in disguise.

But everyday life is not so exciting: Romans simply avoid the routes where the secret policemen stand guard, and this goes double for foreigners. The cafés around the Piazza

Venezia have been deserted, as if the square had become a giant leper colony. The local shops get regular compensation. Empty flats along these routes are rented by the police and their windows bricked up, which is cheaper than keeping them under constant guard. I move around the city much more comfortably, now that I know where not to go. At least I'm this much more at home here now. I can be proud of myself when I recognise a policeman even on the bus, because none of them are so secret that they feel the need to buy a ticket like the rest of us. I can share a sly smile with the people whose conversation dries up when he gets on.

But it's still comforting to hear voices from the old world. Once, coming home, I hear someone cursing creation in Hungarian.

"Good evening," I say. "What's the trouble?"

"My heart, blast the thing, it'll be the death of me. I live here in the first-floor *pensione*, but I can't even make it that far."

"I can help you, I'm a doctor, maybe we can fix it."

"A doctor? Well, you can't fix it, that's for sure, but maybe you're better than these..." his breath runs out.

Somehow or other we make it up to his bed. Lying back, he heaves a sigh of relief. The bluish colour slowly fades from around his lips, he gingerly relaxes the pressure of his elbows against the sides of the bed.

"Do you want me to examine you?" I ask a little tentatively. I can see that it really is his heart, and that it's a complicated case. He waves dismissively.

"Leave it. I have the diagnosis right here in my pocket. Professor What's-his-face wrote it down for me not long ago. The circus referred me to him. They're paying for everything, the circus. It's there in my pocket, take it out."

The diagnosis is as final as the Gestapo's death list. There's nothing left for him to do with that diagnosis but make a will. I hope he doesn't fully understand what it means when all that's left of the aortal flaps is a few morsels of tissue waving helplessly in the bloodstream of his massively expanded arteries... but I can play along as a good doctor should, and so I say:

"Could be worse. You should take digitalis."

My patient lies back on the bed, and now that I've met his heart, he introduces himself by name as well:

"My name is Jurics. I'm the Vice-President of the Maxim Circus. Does my name sound familiar?"

"Jurics...," I say "Jurics?"

"Ah, it's before your time. It's been twenty years since I retired from acrobatics."

"I'll go down to the pharmacy," I say.

"Leave it, stay. Let's chat. I'm better now. It's those damned stairs!"

I can see that he needs a sympathetic ear more than digitalis. A lot of patients are like that, even ones with serious cardiac conditions. The patient wants to talk about themselves because they're always conscious of themselves – reminded, by the weight of their body, of its constant presence, and that it won't be around much longer. They feel that they have a right to talk about themselves, they know that a doctor has to listen. The worst thing to say at a time like this is: "Don't bother, my friend, the lab results say it all". Besides, your diagnosis can even change with the knowledge you pick up – a buzzing in one ear, for example, or that the patient's stomach never could stand canned food.

But Jurics doesn't want to talk about his symptoms. He's not bothered that he is nothing more now than an hourglass running out of sand. What's important to him is the past. What hurts him most is that here is a man who hasn't heard of Jurics, the legendary acrobat.

"Have you ever seen someone jump twelve camels?" he asks me.

"Twelve?"

"No, you haven't," he answers on my behalf, sounding very certain. " Because I'm the only person who's ever done it. Barnum and Bailey signed me in 1912 for five hundred dollars a week. That was when I won the gold medal in Buenos Aires."

I look down at the small, shrivelled, coughing little man with great respect. I press his heel, as if I were looking for the muscle. My finger sticks in its inflamed tissue.

"Oh, I had the muscles all right. And I was quite the gent! I had the first Rolls-Royce in Hungary, doctor."

"Seriously?"

"Absolutely. I bought it in London. I came back with my family. We landed in Trieste, us and the car. We had a driver, fast as the wind. The borderguards just stared. 'May I please examine your papers, your honour?' one of them stuttered eventually. 'I'm not your honour.' My apologies, your grace!' 'I'm not your grace, either.' 'Your highness!' 'Leave it out, I'm a clown, can't you see, a circus acrobat, not some prince!'"

"They didn't believe me. So I got out of the car, just as I was, in my leather jacket, I took a run-up and hop! Did them a double salto over the car, from the back to the front, and over their barrier. Then hop! I jumped back into the car. 'Now do you believe me that I'm a circus man?'" I asked them.

"That's quite a story, they must have been astonished. But let me go get your medicine now."

He won't let me, his story is more important.

"Medicine! Drugs! They're all like that preparation of the druggist of Bahia. At least that worked!"

"For the heart?"

"No, for seasickness."

"Impossible!"

"But it's true. We were coming down from New York, along the Brazilian coast. There was such a storm, it nearly broke the ship in two. Even our seal was unwell, and the parrots were throwing up. Only the captain and the old ship's doctor were still on their feet. That doctor spoke six languages, and cursed in at least twenty-five. He had two hundred patients to look after, and he no longer knew who to comfort in Portuguese and who in English. But he went from one man to the next, and repeated the same thing to us all: "The druggist of Bahia! Tomorrow, we reach Bahia, and the druggist there has a preparation, we ran out of it on the way up – it was choppy too – but he's got a preparation, he gets it form the natives in the jungle. Every year he rides into the heart of the rainforest. What a preparation! It's incredible. You'll see!" All

34

night the two hundred passengers could think of nothing but the druggist of Bahia's preparation, and his sacred name was on everyone's lips constantly. The next day, we arrived. We had no more than two hours, the ship had stopped only to drop off and pick up the post. The ship's doctor ran all the way to the druggist, ran back with two hundred phials of the stuff. Just outside the harbour, the typhoon was blowing nineteen to the dozen while he gave us all the injection. The waves smashed themselves to smithereens on the high sea walls, but even so, the anchored ship was quivering like a nervous mare. We had an hour before we left port".

"And, did it work?"

"It did. The very second we left the lighthouse behind, the wind stopped. We had mirror-smooth seas all the way to Buenos Aires."

"I'll go get your prescription."

"Go tomorrow. I'm feeling sleepy. Here's a hundred lira for the prescription and for your trouble."

A hundred lira! Two weeks' rent! And a wealthy patient to boot! I can finally feel solid ground beneath my feet. Jurics, the acrobat! Maybe there won't be war after all.

Rosenwurz is still up, and he's in a bad mood. They're debating a new law in the Senate: while there's more than a million unemployed in the States, there won't be any visas.

"If I get my visa, we'll have pineapple. And *asti spumante* to wash it down with," he promises.

Chapter VI

Both Mr. Jurics' heart and the political situation are unreliable but I must admit there are also moments of hopefulness. Every now and then, things get better for a little while, and we start to hope. And then sometimes, it seems all the air has been sucked out of the room. I'm sorry for Jurics. My first patient! If only he had typhoid or meningitis, we could fight the disease together. But this, this is treason. His own heart has given up the ghost. And for that, there is no cure or antidote. There's no fighting to be done. There's only the delicate approach, the gentle coaxing of this heart back into the ranks of still-faithful bodily organs.

On his good days, Jurics is forgiving of his heart.

"Oh, if only I hadn't done such huge jumps! All acrobats end this way. The strain! The camels! And the rest. In 1906, we were playing Buffalo. We were staying in the Lafayette hotel, when one night the first floor caught fire. The old wood shack burned like a ring of fire. We, the entire circus staff and fifty more people besides, were stuck up on the eighth floor. We were finished, but for me! There was an eight-meter gap separating us from the flat roof of the building opposite. So I put the springboard up to the window, it was a sprung board, you see, and hop! I jump over to the roof with a rope in my hand. I fixed the rope up on the roof, and the tightrope walkers carried everyone across to safety. All of America was talking about it, and President Roosevelt – not this one, the other one – invited us for lunch at the White House!

"It must have been quite a jump, Mr. Jurics."

"It's not so much the jumping, it's regret that kills the heart. Take my daughter," says the old man and his sudden emotion brings the tears welling up in his eyes, "my own daughter! A hundred thousand *pengős* her dowry was, and I gave her all that jewellery, and my gold medals when she married that general, mind you he was only a captain then. And now she won't so much as look at me – she's ashamed of her old father the clown." He's crying now, the tears falling down his cheeks. "And my son! I left him the circus, I had my own circus you see, and the little crook sold it! Sold my circus, my horses! He bought some land and he's playing the *grand seigneur*. He doesn't write any more, either!"

His son and daughter had left him, and now his heart. Digitalis and coramine won't counteract that. But if he can complain, it already counts as a good day.

In politics, too, there are good days. Rome remains as peaceful as can be. Tourism is booming. Carefree Americans sing the praises of Titian's *Love Sacred and Profane*, jolly Japanese tourists are snapping Bernini's smiling angels on the *Ponte Sant'Angelo*. Douglas Fairbanks sips his maraschino in the Café Greco and goes over to greet the Irish bard.

"The Rose that Never Dies!" cries the old poet.

In the cacophony of languages, the melody of Swedish, the sharp 'i's of Greek, the long 'u' of the Turks, and the 'a's and 'o's of the Italians are all jumbled together. I can hear someone behind me speaking French. I lean back on the Greco's velvet *banquette* and I try to find out what's being said. A gentleman with a lovely clear Parisian accent is holding forth in praise of Victor Hugo and French Romanticism. The man with him has a slight English accent, and one can tell that he's more comfortable with Saxon culture. New thoughts come out of this old contrast; they make statements, then refute them, and measure the greatness of the Greats by their own conversational skill. I try to imagine these two men: the Frenchman must have a goatee, probably some sort of lecturer. I picture the Englishman with swept-back hair and a small pipe.

The mirror opposite brings me up short: the Frenchman is a huge Black man, and the Englishman is a Hindu in a College blazer.

I go over to the "Geographical Society". I see a new face. We introduce ourselves:

"János Bakó, psychiatrist."

"Don't worry," my neighbour whispers, "his real name is Braun, but he wanted to be a surgeon, so he had to change it."

I'm looking for Sommer, but it's too early for him to be here. He usually arrives later with his sparkling ideas and travelogues which carry him, if not from one country to another, at least from that country's embassy to another's. But in the evenings he has other things to do: he's in love with a girl from *Trastevere*. The girl's parents go out for a drink in the evenings, and they leave the little angel – she's only sixteen – locked up. Sommer did three gold fillings for the *concierge*, and so has free access to the staircase of the house. A barred window of the flat opens onto the tiny landing of that staircase. This is where Sommer's love life is played out. Another uncrossable boundary. This is a respectable country, not much has changed since Boccaccio's time.

If the situation is not tense, we talk about medicine. After all, that, too, is a question of life and death. There are triumphs and crises here too. And killings.

In 1938, the ideas about how to kill bacteria were beginning to change. The "Geographical Society" undergoes a happy change to become a "Medical Society" whenever the subject of sulphonamides comes up. Only now are the scientists of the *Institut Pasteur* – Trefnel, Nitti and Bouvet – beginning to explain how this magic drug that cures septicaemia as well as venereal disease, does what it does. Until now, man has wanted to kill bacteria as he would a tiger. But he forgot that his own cells are far more sensitive than the enemy encamped within. If you pump someone's blood full of disinfectants, they won't be able to deal with microorganisms nearly as well. Sulphonamides are wonderdrugs: they don't kill. They quietly disarm the real killer: they take away its hard outer shell, destroy its harmful secretions and then the body itself does the rest. It's an interesting and important lesson: the most deadly weapon is not always the most effective. It's a difficult lesson to learn, for man is a murderous animal.

But Dr. Bakó is not interested in pharmacology. He gets his political insight, as he says, right from the source – the loony bin.

"Let's forget chemistry, economics, and history, gentlemen!" he booms, "Let's be clear about the situation. Don't bother reading the *Times*. Read Kraepelin and Genil-Perrin!"

"Who's Genil-Perrin?" someone asks, I think it's Gyurka Molnár. "Sorry, but I'm a dentist."

"He's the author of the best treatise on paranoia, called '*Les Paranoiaques*'. That's what those British MPs need to understand, not cricket! Let's admit it– insanity is the determining factor of the politics of our age!"

"The white eagle!" the Irish bard waves to us.

"The rose, that never dies!" we reply. "Waiter, a pastry for our great poet!"

Bakó leans on the table as if he were in the pulpit, and I can feel that he's imitating his professor as he begins his little speech:

"Public opinion is nothing but a gigantic house of cards. Man is driven by his evolutionary instinct to ape the opinions of his fellow man. In fact, what really separates him from the apes, who I think also have some respectable opinions, is that by default he wants to think whatever he thinks his fellow-men are thinking. The average German believes in Hitler because he thinks the other Germans already believe in him. It is on this house of cards that the steel framework of the military complex is constructed. Hitler believes in himself, his followers believe in him. Germany bends to the will of this minority. The smaller states around her are forced into following Germany's policies. Europe will join, and Turkey, the house of cards will grow, because everybody wants to be thinking what everyone else is thinking..."

"Yes, that's so" someone says, "...but what was that about paranoia?"

"Just wait. It's my belief... no, my *diagnosis* that the point holding this entire construction together – the keystone, I think it's called – is that Hitler himself is severely mentally ill, with all the visible symptoms of his illness."

"You're not seriously saying that four hundred million people in Europe can catch this mental illness?"

"How many people in Europe have not had measles? Mental illness is contagious too. I know of no-one who's immune to paranoia, but there are lots of people who catch it easily... Shush, dentists! Let me speak!" he says, and re-assumes the professorial pose. "German psychiatrists place the emphasis on paranoid thinking. One fine day, someone thinks everyone's out to get him, that they're all laughing at him. He sees conspiracy all about him. The conspiracy grows and grows, every cyclist or every bald man becomes a member, until the hunted man asks himself: why are they after me? Why are they so many? Then comes the answer: because I am a great man, an artist, a politician, God, a Prophet, an actor. And the patient goes off to preach or play politics, or just simply to fight the grand conspiracy. In this fight, he is the most logical being. As my beloved professor used to say, the paranoiac sets his pieces up wrong, but then plays chess beautifully with them. He starts with a mystery and ends in logic."

"And the French? Genil-Perrin?"

"He approaches the question from another direction altogether: he says that the patient builds his pie in the sky on four pillars – pride, uncertainty, faulty judgement, and cognitive dissonance. His pride is often his most important and best-hidden quality. Ludendorff didn't use his aristocratic 'von', and it seemed to be out of humility, right up until it turned out he thought he was Wotan![1] Hitler wears a simple uniform with only his iron cross for decoration. Not like that creep, Göring, who's sane, but looks like a walking jeweller's. As for uncertainty, the gentlemen of the Gestapo could explain that better than I can: that's why the environment of the paranoiac doesn't change, and false judgement provides the misty basis for logical acts. This is the world of ideologies. That's why you can't argue with the paranoiac: when you get him cornered, he falls back on his dogma, and becomes invulnerable. And as for cognitive dissonance, it is the very key to the paranoid personality: it can't bear the world. And so it retreats into the monastery, hermitage, or lighthouse."

"That would be a good job, being a lighthouse keeper," Gyurka Molnár interrupts, "somewhere in New Zealand…"

"Into a tower," Bakó resumes, "and that's the most elegant form of self-medication. The patient is at once healed in his tower, because no matter how much pride he has, no matter his mysticism and dissonance, there's no-one there for him to torture. But God help us if the paranoiac, and luckily there's not so many of them, wants to change the world they can't stand! If they want to drive out its shady conspiracies, the devil, or as Don Quixote said, *los encantadores*, the Jesuits, or freemasons, or Jews, or Blacks, or foreigners, or speculators. Then the persecuted becomes the prophet of persecution, and fights, and this is the chief symptom of his sickness: nothing can shake him. He is always right. No crime burdens his conscience, because it is always his victim who is the guilty party. The paranoiac, before committing whatever crime, ceremonially shifts all the blame onto his victim. And that's why these paranoias are so suited to becoming religions; they give their adherents a clean conscience, too."

[1] King of the Gods in old German myths and in Richard Wagner's Ring Cycle.

"I'd like to know whether it's worth bothering to wait for Sommer," Molnár interrupts again. "You see, the Cocos Islands..."

But once he's got going, Bakó can't be quieted.

"What the world needs is a committee of psychiatrists periodically to examine the mental health of the leading politicians. That's what we need instead of the League of Nations. I can already see the experts talking about markets, military potential and I don't know what other idiocies, when they're really talking about us! But they're not paranoiacs, they're just straight stupid. Madness as a factor in politics is the curse of our century, and no-one can take that away from us! There have been mass movements based on paranoia in the past, but the flagellants didn't have a weekly paper, didn't have Radio Flagellant blaring out their message twenty-four hours a day, an eternal trumpet blowing their tune. If the *Wiedertaufer*s and the Hussites had invented the loudspeaker! You can't manufacture a real mass-paranoia with a few standard bearers, but now Goebbels has the tools. And it's possible in America, too. Even a paranoid head of state can get better, and as a doctor, I tell you it's his sacred right to try, as it is every patient's. It's with reason he feels better when people treat him like a god, he feels confident as long as he can trust his police; his principles are not false if they are accepted as legal tender, and he has nothing but time for the people kissing his feet. The paranoiac treated this way, like a god, is cured.

"Heil Hitler!" someone says. Needless to say, there are Germans in the Greco too, more and more of them, in fact. They don't belong to any of the "geographical societies", but they say much the same things as they sip their coffees:

"That sort of thing doesn't happen at home."

"Mussolini?" someone in the group asks.

"He's normal. He's a perfectly sane crook, an adventurer," the adjunct-professor declares. "I can vouch for him any day. What he needs," he says, and thumps his chest, "is not the madhouse but a good thrashing. No, *speriamo bene.*"

I'd happily go on listening to our renowned expert, but Rosenwurz is calling me over.

"Come," he shouts above the din, "I need you, you speak English. I need you to write a short letter for me. Come home, or would you prefer a coffee first?" I'd prefer to wait for Sommer, but he won't let me. "Come on," he whispers, "it's about that dinner of ours…"

"In other words, a visa matter?"

"Yes, of course, the affidavit, what else?"

I get the details back in Rosenwurz's room: the quota's fine, but he needs an American citizen to vouch that our Mr Rose won't be a burden on the forty-eight states. Unfortunately, he doesn't know any American citizens, but the "geographicals" told him what to do: write to an American with the same name. The trouble is, there are very few Americans with his distinctive name.

"If you're called Cohen, it's better," he says sadly.

But in any case, he's found someone with a similar name, I write his details on the envelope: Mr Morton Rosenstingl, 159 Holland Ave, The Bronx, New York, N.Y. Rosenwurz caresses the addressed envelope lovingly while he dictates.

My dear Sir!

I am a "wurz", while you are a "stingl", but, my dear Sir, you and I are grown from a single rose-stem. You are doubtless the better branch. I beg you to let me have that form, the affidavit, that would allow me to sail across the ocean, so wide today, though perhaps not wide enough tomorrow, that separates us. My dear Sir, I swear to you I will not be a burden to you. I will never ask you for anything again. I'll take any work, I'll be a gravedigger, I'll drive trucks transporting high explosives, I'll go repair the tops of the skyscrapers, because that way, at least, I am master of my fate. Sir, I am a decent man, decorated with the Iron Cross First Class in the Great War.

"I think we should leave that out," I tell him.

"Put it in. Hitler's only got the Second Class."

"So…'in the Great War'…"

"'Believe me, my dear Sir, I would take any job, I'd even go be a Negro. All I ask, my dear Sir, is that you send it today, before it's too late. I beg you, Sir.' That's enough."

"I beg you, Sir. That's it. That's what we needed. This time, I'm sure the visa will go through. It'll be a fine supper. Here, in the house, it's *gemütlich* that way. Cheese, butter, salami we'll have. Thank you, and goodnight."

Chapter VII

Jurics' heart is bad, the political situation is worse, but my financial situation is the worst of all. I can now count the number of days until my last lira is spent. I'm saving wherever I can, I hardly eat a thing, but the fact of being alive is in itself ruining me financially: I have a roof above my head and sleep in a bed! This, today, counts as a luxury. Many hundreds of families are living in the thin strips of border between countries, and tomorrow the number of displaced could stretch into the thousands. One has to pay for one's luxuries. Jurics owes me money, but I daren't bring it up. After all, it was I who told him to avoid all forms of stress.

Despite my dire financial situation, my social network is growing. A lot of people come and go in the Greco, and Lewis introduces them all to each other. That is his daily bread, or rather, pastry. I shake hands with a Swedish painter who's just rented a Hungarian colleague's studio in the via Margutta for three months. I drink punch with Monsignor Cabillaud, with his snow-white hair. He is a wise French abbott, whose sense of calm is so great that it would seem he stepped out of some old painting on a wall somewhere of an afternoon only to come and smoke a little mortal cigar with the elegant ghosts of the Café Greco, and then make his way back, by evensong, to his home above the altar of the church of Saint Louis. I secretly hope he'll invite me to his church one day to play the organ.

"I like the French," I tell him sincerely.

"My grandfather liked Zola, my mother swore by Jean-Christophe, and I wait on Georges Duhamel's words with adulation. Oh, Salavin! Oh, the *Chronique des Pasquiers*! Every European has two languages – his mother tongue, and French," the abbé notes proudly.

"But you have three, with Latin."

"Ah, but you have four, with the language of Music," he returns.

I like Monsignor Cabillaud because he is unruffled by the winds of our time. The Church Fathers stand between him and bad news. I can see that he's stronger than the events around him.

My Italian vocabulary is growing too. I notice it when I start talking to Francesca, Elsa's maid. The poor thing burnt her face forty years ago. Her nose is altogether gone, her mouth is awry, and one eye only opens halfway. That ancient flame took her facial cues, that magic remnant of pre-Babel communication. I hardly dared move my own features faced with her immobile ones, just as my eyes close when I find myself with a blind person, and my movements slow with a Parkinson's patient; so we used to avoid each other in silence. Now, we get on.

I have completed Attilio's course. I am now graduating to secondary school, so to speak, and Aldo di Naso is my teacher. I am moving beyond grammar alone.

Aldo has time. Mussolini has gone north, travelling around and giving speeches. The employees of the Ministry of Propaganda get to catch up on their sleep. The Ministry takes care of itself. The speech, even if it's only a few sentences, fills up the front page of the newspapers. The third and fourth pages are given over to a dissection of the domestic and international repercussions of the 'sacred sermon'. The second page, as it should be, belongs to the local news. And so the propaganda takes care of itself.

As for the "International Implications of the Speech" section, that's not a problem, either: the decision over whether there'll be war or there'll be peace rests in the hands of two men. It's in the secret recesses of two brains that those – probably chemical – processes are going on that will determine what is to come for the proteins of many millions of bodies. And as a body will become paralysed if blood gets into a few dozen cells, so humanity may become paralysed if the blood rises in those two brains: an unimaginable amount of physical and emotional suffering depends on the precise combination of words that lie in the coils of the Broca's area of two brains. Bakó says one of those brains isn't healthy. It's understandable that people the world over pore over the speeches the way wise men once pored over the Apocalypse of St John. Newspapers everywhere give their opinion of the commentary the speeches arouse. A library's worth of books can be written about a single sentence here or there. Writers puzzle over exactly what the Leader meant when he said "if". The Ministry of Propaganda can relax.

But what if the Duce says nothing? Yesterday, he said: "And now, my soldiers, I will be silent. From now on, it is actions that will speak."

"What'll you do then?" I ask.

"We'll go to work."

"I don't understand. What do you do in the Ministry of Propaganda? Huge countries get along just fine without a Ministry of Propaganda. And yet you employ three thousand people?"

"Not at all. There's six thousand seven hundred of us. But really we're understaffed. So we use external consultants, translators, advisors. Believe me, out of the fourteen ministries, we're the only one that actually does any work at all! Just look at what those crooks in the Ministry of African Affairs do with all their time!"

He pulls out a wad of documents and files from his briefcase.

"They maintain fourteen journals of their own, but that's not the worst of it. Let them take care of that, at least that's one less thing for us to do. No, the worst of it is that they send us their proclamations!"

"Why?"

"So we can send them on to the world press! To journals like 'Italy's Peaceful Conquests', 'The Youngest Empire in the World', and 'The Progress of Civilization'. We write a commentary to go with the decrees, highlight why they're important, or at least put them into a form the public can understand. Look, here's the new regulations for the fish market in Tripoli... a bit of background to help you along: previously, the way it worked was that the fishermen fished, and then

45

they sold the fish they caught. Just any old how, in a completely individualistic way, however they felt like, not caring a damn for order and the state! But that's all over now. They've set up a fish market in Tripoli. The first paragraph of the proclamation sets out who can sell fish, and what kind of fish they can sell. Needless to say, licences to sell fish are distributed first to veteran members of the Party, war cripples, war widows, fathers with large families, etc. There's a whole established procedure for that sort of thing, as there is for porters and ministers, and it has just as many unwritten exceptions to it as those other two. The second paragraph goes on to describe how to purchase the fish: the fish has to be weighed in the presence of a regulator, its price calculated, and then the central till makes out two copies of the receipt, on which the weight, type, and price of the fish are shown. One has to be handed back to the fishmonger; the other constitutes the fish' papers if you want to take it out into the town. If you're caught carrying a fish without papers, they know you bought it on the black market, and you go straight to jail."

"And what do you do in all this?"

"We just issue a release entitled 'The Reform of the Tripoli Fish Trade'. We've managed to solve an age-old problem. The citizens of Tripoli will from now on receive their staple food in a legal manner, according to fascist principles... and then we show a few pictures of the market."

"What good does that do?"

Aldo is vexed that I can't even understand the simple things.

"Has anyone ever written about the fish market in New Orleans? Has anyone ever said that the distribution of fish in Bergen is the pride of the Constitutional Monarchy? No! Because America and Norway don't have Ministries of Propaganda. Christ started with only twelve disciples!" Aldo shouts. "Who were they? They were his Ministers of Propaganda! Saint Ignatius, Saint Francis were nothing but propagandists! Saint Francis even spoke to the fish! In the beginning was Propaganda. Not even God was satisfied with just creating the world, he had a book written about it, and if he hadn't we wouldn't know where we came from, and who we have to thank for everything we have to be thankful for that isn't thanks to fascism!"

I thank him for the lesson, and go see Jurics. He's not at all well, poor thing. His colleague, Monihuello, the Spanish ventriloquist, is sitting beside him.

"Doctor," he says, "I won't last much longer. I want to make a will. Please, go and find me another Hungarian, it'll only take five minutes, but I need two witnesses. I want to make a will in Hungarian."

"I'll fetch a Hungarian from the Greco."

János Bakó is once more preaching to the assembled when I arrive:

"The difference between the pharmaceutical industry and the pharmacy is decisive: the drug companies would be finished if only sick people bought drugs. They have to shovel aspirin into the healthy. The vast majority of humanity is more or less bodily healthy, you can't build up big business based on the sick alone. But pharmacies are another matter. There, you'd be an idiot to base your business on the sane – it's the paranoiacs who rule the roost and because they've got all the other poor fools in their power!"

Sommer arrives at the same time as me. I want to grab him and take him to Jurics.

"Just a second," he says, "boys! I've got it – I know how we'll get the American visa. More than that, I know how we'll get citizenship!"

"Don't jump the gun, see what the Dalai Lama has to say," Bakó retorts, because he hates being interrupted.

"No, I'm serious, boys! According to American law, everyone who suffers a shipwreck on their coastline gets automatic citizenship."

"Go on, then, Sommer, you'll be the happiest shipwrecked sailor in history!"

"The question is really the following: can we get a captain to wreck his ship on the American coast? It seems unlikely. But we could rent a rowboat for the purpose. After all, even Columbus crossed the Ocean in a nutshell. And once we get to the American coast, there's bound to be suitable rocks and things."

"Come on, Sommer" I say, "Jurics might be dead by now."

We go back, it's barely a five minute walk. Jurics is not only still alive, he's feeling better. He introduces himself to Sommer, camels and all. We start the testamentary process. Jurics dictates, I write, Sommer is the witness, the ventriloquist is silent.

"I, Ferenc Jurics, being of sound mind and body, do will regarding all my fixed and liquid assets as follows…"

I'm curious as to what the old poor man can have left.

"First of all: my twelve room villa on the Ménesi út in Budapest, land registry number 34568/II.2, together with its associated garden, I leave to the Hungarian Union of Artists, of which I was for years the Honorary President. This should be their home for old artists."

He has a villa!

"This platinum ring I wear on my finger, with the diamond, which was a gift to me from the director of my beloved circus, Mr Maxim, I give back to him, together with the gold Schaffhausen hunter watch in my suitcase, and its chain."

He has a watch!

"My suitcase, my clothes and my winter coat, I leave to the landlady."

"The landlady, got it."

"I wish to divide the 120,000 lira in my bank account as follows: 100,000 lira to be divided equally between the artists and staff of the Maxim Circus, 10,000 lira for Miss Mucci, who has always shown me such kindness…"

"…kindness…"

"and a further 10,000 lira to my trusted doctor, who is also witness to my last will and testament."

(Five thousand meals, I translate to myself mechanically).

At that moment, Jurics' lips go blue. His facial expression changes, he sits up in bed, and breaks out in a cold sweat. I reach for his injection, but he stops me.

"Write!" he orders, "Write this: my daughter, Berta Hatay Hata, the wife of General Hatay Hata, I hereby disown! She has cruelly betrayed her father, and I have nothing to leave her, even as I stand at death's door, but a curse upon her head!"

"King Lear," Sommer whispers, and at that moment, Jurics, with his matted hair, does indeed resemble the Shakespearean hero.

"My son, that haughty crook, I also disown!" he shouts, completely exhausted, and falls back onto his pillow.

"I now commend my soul to God," he adds ceremoniously in the silence.

"Amen," says a mysterious voice somewhere under the bed. "What was that?"

The Spanish ventriloquist blushes, and repeats, this time moving his lips:

"Amen…"

Chapter VIII

I can understand how a prince regent must feel – they love their father, but they'd like to rule. A doctor can be exposed to the same conundrum – especially if his last hope, his single bearer's bond, is his only patient's last will and testament. Needless to say, I will do everything I can to extend his life as long as possible. Every eight hours, I give him a quarter of a milligram of strophantine dissolved in warm sucrose. I'm there three times a day, I boil the needle, I massage Jurics' swollen liver, I do my humble rounds to the grocer's, bring his fresh water for him. He's my first serious patient, and every extra day he lives is thanks to me. But what if the Professor was wrong? What if the strophantine works miracles? I've seen patients like him last for months – and I don't have that long, I could end up on the street any day now. If only he would give me a small advance, say two hundred lira! But I can't bring myself to ask him for an advance on his own death!

I go to the pharmacy, I spend my evenings with Jurics, I don't even go to the Greco anymore. All I know is that the situation is grave. The British fleet is being assembled in home waters. Platoons of soldiers march through the city. "*Speriamo bene*", people sigh.

Jurics doesn't have much to lose if there's a war, but he's not happy either. War is bad for the Circus.

49

"The last war was enough trouble," he tells me. "It caught us in Ostend, the whole troupe. The Belgians arrested us, put us all on a truck. The horses, the elephant and the giraffe marched alongside. It was night, it was raining. All of a sudden, I jumped – hop! – out of the truck and onto the back of the giraffe, and hop! off we went into the great outdoors. The guards just stared as I galloped for the Dutch border on my giraffe. You know, there's not a horse alive that could catch a giraffe at full gallop, let alone our magnificent Congo, and they didn't have motorcycle policemen back then, that's how I got away... You'll see," he continues, "the Brits will win again. They're tough boys, they are! You know, I'd really love to live long enough to see them get Mussolini and Hitler. God forbid they should hang them! The Circus would pay their weight in gold for them. They could sing duets. What a number that would be! My dear boy, we'd be rich! And we'd treat them humanely, like we do the other animals."

Jurics is the reason I can't write more precisely now about the events of the time. I, who lived through it, could not tell you the story of the Munich conference. The person who lives through something is not always the most faithful witness: on the hundredth anniversary of the Battle of Borodino, they presented a one hundred and twelve year old *muzhik* to the Tsar.

"Ah, and you're the man who took part in the battle?"

"Yes, *vase velitchestvo.*"

"And do you remember the battle?"

"Oh yes, *vase velitchestvo.*"

"Did you see Napoleon?"

"Oh, I held the reins of his horse, I was his groom."

"And how did the Emperor look?"

"He had a long, snow-white beard, *vase velitchestvo.*"

All I took away from the Munich conference were the big words – Chamberlain getting out of the aeroplane with his umbrella: "Peace for our time!" A member of Parliament called Churchill saying: "You were given the choice between war and dishonour. You chose dishonour, and you will have war". And I recall a picture: Hitler's and Mussolini's hats hanging next to each other on a rack in a vestibule somewhere. These are the scales of fate, the symbols of power. It is right and proper that such hats should preside over the stuffed shirts below.

Bakó was analysing the situation, and to enhance his professorial air, he had donned a pair of spectacles.

"Let the psychologist speak!" he declared in a tone of voice that would brook no opposition. "In the name of psychology, I hereby predict the fall of the dictatorships!"

The faces of the audience do not reflect his optimism.

"Historical processes are played out according to the rules governing the behaviour of proteins: they are limited by time and space. As regards their timing, it was President Lincoln who put it best. In fact, it's the enduring shame of the profession that a common-or-garden President should have been the one to formulate such a fundamental truth: 'You can fool a few people for a long time, many people for a short time, but not all people for all times'. That sideburned sage was the first to discover the relationship between historical processes and the actors in them."

"It's a shame Sommer's still sitting in his cage, he's always late," Gyurka Molnár says.

"Listen to *me*, your neck's on the line too, you know! The paranoiac who starts the process of *fooling the people* puts a certain amount of power into it. Simple mechanics tells us that the movement thus occasioned will eventually stop. But that's just an analogy rather than a description of the process. Something else happens among the proteins: antibodies take over the role of friction, and start a long process of immunisation. In the whole body, as in the single cell. If you don't understand gonorrhoea, you won't understand politics."

"Oh, you've had it, have you?"

"Fools! Can't one talk seriously to you, either, any more? Try to understand: only a few cells take part in the development of gonorrhoea, the paltry few million cells of the mucous membrane. They're the backbone of the whole thing. But if we administer a vaccine, we get the billions of cells of the whole body on our side, and it goes away. Or, if you insist on a mechanical analogy, for I know that simple souls never make it past mechanics, a big avalanche travels faster than a little snowball. The spirit of a monastery will remain because a few dozen people maintain it. Fashions change. A Lindbergh craze can captivate two hundred million people and be over three weeks later. There's a similar motive energy behind each, but the crowd absorbs it, it dissipates in the crowd. The enthusiasm of the crowd is greater than that of the group: '*Er wünscht sich einen grossen Kreis, um ihm gewisser zu erschütten*' Goethe's actor says, while Schiller responds sadly, '*Dem Mimen flicht die Nachwelt keine Kränze*".

"German literature: outstanding," someone calls cheekily.

"Comportment unsatisfactory!" the Professor responds harshly. "What's all this about Munich? Dictatorships spread, they capture more and more people. But you can't fool all the people all of the time! Not for all times! Listen: there's seventy million people in Germany. An average person says hello five times a day. That makes three hundred and fifty million 'Heil Hitlers' a day. In a single year, Germany produces three hundred and sixty five times three hundred and fifty million 'Heil Hitlers', and in ten years, ten times that amount, but actually people say hello more than five times a day. It's just something we have to get used to, like Mussolini's chin. The barber's union decided years ago to hang his picture in all the barber's shops. The shoeshines followed suit. Then bars. The only two places where one can avoid it is in Church or in the brothel, and I am convinced that this is the root cause of the popularity of both. Perhaps that's why the monarchs of old put their face on the coinage, because even people who find them disgusting rarely go so far as throwing money away. But these dictators go too far! I'll bet you that three days after his fall, you won't be able to find a really good, black-shirted, ostrich-plumed, saber-rattling photo of him for love nor money."

Bakó, then, is satisfied. His logic, however, leaves the assembled company cold. Not even Sommer's late arrival (as usual) improves the mood – especially since tonight, our noted explorer is withdrawn.

"No more kidding around, now it's serious. Tomorrow," he adds, as if to give weight to his words, "I'm going in to Rühössy, to see if he'll extend my passport."

If Sommer is going in to see Rühössy, the situation must be grave indeed.

The assiduous reader, for whom it is impossible from these lines to grasp the real significance of Munich, should not even try. By reading the German and Italian newspapers, one can get a good idea of the mood and opinions of these two peoples. Newspapers, knowing that people are happy to pay to see their opinions in print, have attempted to pour into words the popular mood – and by doing so, have helped shape it. Newspapers in dictatorships do not seek to inform public opinion, but to make it. Their goal is to manufacture an artificial opinion. But in Italy, they've failed.

A new discipline was born – the science of reading the papers. This science is comparable to chess theory or the higher forms of dogma. The reader reads the news, attempts to reconstruct the actual event, and from the difference between the event and the way it's presented, tries to deduce which way the political wind is currently blowing. It's the same method a mathematician might use, given an object's dimensions and the shape of its mirror image, to determine the degree of deformation of the mirror. In this instance, though, it is a malleable and ever-changing mirror in which events are reflected, and it was this daily quest to find the curvature of the mirror that future generations will be hard pressed to understand or learn. To do this proficiently, one also needed to be able to look at events in the differently curved, or less curved, mirrors of the foreign papers – and that meant twelve hours of hard labour a day.

It was easier for the employees of the workshop that bent the mirror this way and that, like my friend Aldo di Naso. It's thanks to his trust that I got a little insight into a smaller, but still instructive affair, in compensation for my dozing through Munich. Readers of the *Messagero* and the *Giornale d'Italia* of the time will no doubt recall the incident.

The Munich agreement was not really much of a victory for Italy. We mustn't forget that Italian-Czech diplomatic relations had been close indeed, especially while an independent Austria buffered the borders of both. But when Austria fell, and Italy, under the name of the *passo romano*, introduced the

German *stechschritt*, or goose-step, their mutual interests no longer aligned. Nonetheless, the inscription on the tomb of the unknown soldier still preserved the inscription recording the names of the Czech Legions who had fought "for the Italian people and our common victory". Germany's progress gave no advantage to the 'fascist motherland'; only a French defeat would lead to real gains. But that was not to be rushed by overhasty forcefulness, no – first, the Western democracies had to be lulled into quietude by 'peace for our time'.

One path only therefore remained open to Aldo and his colleagues, and that was to make of Munich a personal triumph for the 'snow-browed, iron-fisted' man – or rather MAN, as he was capitalised – who had 'stopped the chariots of war'. But this in itself was not enough – it was hard to embellish the everyday songs of praise already in existence. The Duce's trip to the north had already exhausted the Italian language's otherwise rich fund of laudatory epithets. The Emperor (and King) had already visited his iron chancellor's birthplace. He had already received every conceivable decoration. The "founder and generalissimo of the Imperium" was poor fodder for the perpetual motion machine that was the Ministry of Propaganda.

There was nothing for it but to divert the attention of the newspaper-reading public, momentarily in a good mood thanks to the temporary putting off of war, to the size of their Imperium. The underlying thesis was the following: everything that happened could only serve to strengthen this young, new (but built on ancient foundations) and peaceable (but mighty) Imperium. Half of Africa was now Italian. All of North Africa could become part of the *mare nostrum* system. The Duce must have to hand the sword of Islam (made in Florence), so that standing at the edge of the desert he can flash the sun along its glittering blade. If the Germans are looking to Prague, let us look to Mecca! In other words, the Ministry of Propaganda asked the Duce (who kept Pandora's box in the ping-pong room of the former Austro-Hungarian embassy to the Holy See), in a personal – and highly secret – note, to comment "on his feelings if they were to build a big mosque in Rome". The image of towering minarets appeared in the Duce's Caesarean imagination, and with the handwriting he borrowed from D'Annunzio and the succinctness he'd learned from Napoleon, wrote a simple '*approvato*' on the submission. And so the affair of the Roman mosque began.

How does a poor lonely foreigner find out what goes on in the secret deliberations of the world's most closely guarded man? This is another thing that makes sense only in Rome. Other than the eternal mystery of the Holy Mass, there are hardly any secrets here. The future is a secret, of course, like anywhere else. Little girls, emerging from their girlhood, have secrets – great, pure, and holy secrets. The earth has its secrets, Venuses perhaps, or round metal coins. But the Palazzo Venezia has no secrets – every secret policeman sells secrets. Ministers tell the most secret secrets of state to their most secret of secret girlfriends. Everyone here is confessor and confessant. The Ministry of Propaganda occasionally propagates real news as well. Aldo's boss talked to the Minister's secretary's best friend. I know all about the affair of the mosque before the *Times*' sharpest hack.

He only got hold of the story the next day from the following newspaper article: the Imam of Tripoli and the Benghazi Mufti, in conjunction with the Union of Muslim Students in Rome have written to His Excellency the Minister for African Affairs, to ask him to grant them permission to build a small, modest mosque in Rome. It's just a little piece in the paper, but quite a coincidence.

The newspapers then relay His Excellency's response: "The Minister assured the Muslim dignitaries that he will do everything in his power – though modest it may be – to help them". This is followed by a brief explanation – the Minister, in true fascist fashion, always does whatever he can to help.

On the third day, the news makes the front page: "The Minister has contacted the Governor of Rome in the matter of the mosque". The Palestinian Arab daily, *Mufurc Akhtar*, asks: "Is there to be a mosque in Rome?" The *Völkischer Beobachter* carries a small item: "The Arab world looks with interest to the matter of the Roman mosque".

It is traditional, before the feasts of the great saints, to have triduums and novenas. Three days of this was enough. On the fourth day, huge headlines announced:

"The Duce has decided! The Imperium's four million Muslims shall have their mosque in Rome!"

The Duce's word cannot be without an echo. This echo drowned out everything else for a week. Like the sound of a pistol shot in a mine, it reverberates from every side.

The tone is thankful. If the press is the mirror of the truth, then the citizens of a totalitarian state live in a permanent ecstasy of thankfulness anyway. But this time, their thankfulness knows no bounds. The telegram of thanks from the Muslims of Tunis reads: "To you, O Duce, we owe our thanks for the granting of this longstanding wish of ours – the mosque in Rome will be a marble pillar on the road to glory..." Not to mention the messages from the Iraqi Dervishes and the President of the Muslim League of India...

The effect is aided, according to the law of musical counterpoint, by the harmonious chiming of the diverse individual elements – and this is where the real art comes in, where the disparate notes of reality are melded, according to a specific conception, into a new and complete form. The Tunisian weekly, *El Biribi* has this to add to the Muslim League: "The sword of Islam glittering in the Duce's hand gives new hope to the Muslims languishing under the rule of the British Mandate..." The *Pakistan Times* responds: "The foundation of the mosque in Rome is a great occasion for expressing Arab solidarity. Our brothers in Tunis appreciated our efforts..."

The *Messagero's* front page declares: "According to the Muslims gathered in the Gül Baba mosque, the co-operation between the Indian Muslim League and the Muslims of Tunis may have far-reaching consequences in the future. The Albanian faithful at Gül Baba greeted the news of the gathering with joy..."

Aldo and his colleagues are nose to the grindstone, and there's plenty of work at the Italian consulates too... with the result that by the next day, the story is front-page news. By this point, the readership is waiting for the authorised version of the outcome; the moral of the story. Virginio Gayda, the leader-writer of the *Giornale d'Italia* holds forth in a simplified version of D'Annunzio's style. "The Duce's mouthpiece," whisper those in the know. Those even more in the know, know that he is nothing but a glorified typewriter – willing and able to write thirty, two hundred or two thousand lines about any subject under the sun, and then refute what he's just written succinctly, or at length. For this reason, he's known as a man with considered opinions, free of the slightest taint of fascism.

"The Roman Mosque," he writes, "is a symbol of the expansion of the Imperium into Africa. Treading the path of the Roman legions, fascist Italy has reached the walls of Carthage. Rome, the mother of civilisation, was always sensitive to the cultures of the peoples she conquered – just look at the mosque-like dome of the Pantheon, where the gods assembled around the statue of Caesar, where the faithful would bow down before the Tomb of the Unknown God. And what could be a more eloquent symbol of the reincarnation of this ancient empire than the Duce's personal effort to create a refuge for the Muslim spirit, threatened as it is by the world's plutocracies, under his own benevolent eye..."

The monolithic headlines in the *Tevere* scream of scandal: "Why wasn't there a mosque in Rome before? The real background to the story!

"For years – nay, decades – our Muslim subjects have been labouring to realise that plan so dear to all Muslim fascists, the construction of a mosque in Rome. But until now, the Jews have successfully pre-empted the fulfilment of the rights of the Arabs. The freemasons as early as 1902 "bought" the plot then intended to house the mosque and built tennis courts on it..."

The German press, needless to say, quotes from *Tevere* and indeed goes one further: "The Roman paper *Tevere* uncovers the Jewish plot raging in Italy, which until today has prevented it... but the Duce's fist has struck!" The *Times* judges dispassionately: "After the mosques in London, Paris, and Budapest, it would seem that Rome is to house a similar institution. It is too early as yet to judge regarding the possible political implications". The French reaction is a number of caricatures, which Aldo brings home one night from the Ministry: Mussolini at the top of a minaret singing "la ilah il Allah, Mussolini rasum lulla", with camels and dervishes goose-stepping past below. The Italian caricaturists join the fray: an ageing, fat, saggy-breasted France is shown sitting on the Arabs. And another image: a blackshirted, grinning giant is building a mosque, and Arabs are rushing to join him from every direction.

King Fuad offers carpets, the Carrara marble works a fountain. The Sultan of Zanzibar is to send five hundred pairs of leather slippers for the use of visitors to the mosque. Maybe the Munich conference didn't happen after all. All anyone's talking about now is minarets.

The excitement reaches fever pitch when an anonymous article appears in the stolid columns of the *Osservatore Romano:*

"Under the Terms of the Lateran Treaty, his Holiness the Pope accepted the Sovereignty of the Italian State over the city of Rome, which since the time of St Peter has been the seat of Christianity. In the spirit of this agreement, Italy became the guardian of this sacred tradition, and undertook to protect the ruins that bear testimony to the martyrdom of the saints. The special nature of this city makes it impossible that there should be inconsiderate demolition or construction within its walls for purely political reasons. Nothing can overshadow the centuries-long struggle of the Popes to protect Western civilisation and the Holy Church, in which the battle of Lepanto and the siege of Malta were not the final word. Remembering these glorious victories in no way prejudices others' rights to culture or life, but it can serve as a useful reminder to those who would sacrifice the sacred treasures of Rome for their own short-term interests."

The Italian press does not deem the thought worthy of a single drop of ink; it doesn't make reference to the mosque, or even to fascism. But the Germans trumpet it, as if this were all they had been waiting for.

Goebbels, with his bandy legs, gets to preaching, along the lines of the Biblical example of forgiveness for those who convert on their death-beds: "Whoever is still blind to the behind-the-scenes machinations of the Jewish-Catholic alliance, can now open their eyes. Even the simplest among them can now see what the goal of this satanic compact against the rising nations is."

The *Times* poses the question: "Disagreement between the Vatican and the Italian Government?" The *Tevere* rails against "dark powers". *Racial Purity* brings an interesting new element to the discourse, discovering "Aryan elements among the Arabs of Tripoli", as well as finding "Lombard blood among the natives of Bizerte".

"The mood," Aldo says, "is ripe. We can now organise the laying of the foundation stone."

The Greco reacts to these events in its own way – the German "Geographical Society" debates them with pleasure: the Pope will finally see that fascism is not the bastion guarding Christianity against Communism. It shows the true value of the Lateran Accords, and is the rightful recompense for the Concordat with the Germans".

At the doctors' table, Gyurka Molnár is telling jokes.

"The rose, that never dies", the poet declares.

But Rosenwurz is past caring. In a corner of the newspaper free of mosques, he has read that a postal service aeroplane has crashed between Bermuda and New York.

"My letter!" he sighs. "With my luck, my letter was bound to be on that plane! If the affidavit isn't here in eight days, I have to wait for another quota!" Then he adds, "Pheasant, pineapple, venison, goose, whipped cream and chocolate cake!"

Chapter IX

Foods leave me. Ice-cream was the first to go. Ripe, yellow pears, fragrant melons, and the sweet grapes of the Italian soil were next. The *rosticcerias* roast their meat for others, but not for me. Grilled meats no longer so much as looked at me any more. *Pasta asciutta* was my most faithful companion – it was one lira twenty opposite the central post office. But even its place has now been taken by bean, carrot, or cabbage soup (seventy-five cents), and it was this soup that kept me going through the Munich crisis. By the start of the mosque affair, even this had made way for that flat, salty bread smothered in hot oil called *pizza*, of which the baker-herbseller will cut you off a large square for twenty cents. This remains my companion throughout the next weeks. It's the energy stored in these pizza squares that keeps me moving, waiting for something to happen. A gypsy woman once told me that a man would come into my life, and that from then on, everything would be ok. Could it be Jurics?

Jurics has been noticeably better since he made his will. He might even, hop!, jump right out of the claws of death. He reproaches me viciously if I'm five minutes late. For ten thousand lira, he has a right to expect punctuality.

At the moment, I don't even have money to buy a newspaper. It's Aldo who fills me in on the current events in world history, but every second day I can go through the *Times* at the café Aragno. This gives me the opportunity to get acquainted with the Ladies of Malta. They're not particularly young, nor particularly stylish, but then again, they're off duty. They, too, often read the *Times,* and sometimes I have to wait for them to finish.

"The Royal Oak," says one, "will you look at that!"

"I know it. I once shot a blue fox on that ship."

I listen in brazenly on their conversation. They chat away merrily, about clothes for picking up men in, about distant colleagues, and about the passing of Frigyes Karinthy.

"I left my Karinthy and Zilahy books in La Valetta!"

"Oh, Rühössy'll authorise another trip, don't worry."

"If only his hands weren't always so moist. I hate sweaty men."

Sommer isn't a fan of Rühössy either. I find out, indirectly, that he really has been to the consulate. They went together with Gyurka Molnár and Péter Pogány (whom I don't know) to get their passports renewed.

"I'll need to see your parents', and your grandparents' birth certificates, as well as their baptismal certificates, and such documents as will verify their places of residence over the past fifty years," Rühössy told them. "Only then will I be able to issue your certificate of nationality, with which you will be able to renew your passports."

"But your Excellency," Sommer began, being not so bold at the Hungarian consulate as at all the others, "I want to emigrate. We're undesirable persons. I'm asking you to make it possible for us to emigrate – we'll go all the way to the jungle."

"Your travel plans are no concern of mine. I will only renew the passports of Hungarian citizens."

"But we are Hungarian!"

"You are not. You are persons whose native language happens to be Hungarian."

A deep silence followed. Then Gyurka Molnár blurted out: "But we always support the Hungarian football team!"

The only reason Rühössy didn't tell the lot of them to go to hell right then and there is that they would have needed their passports renewed to get there. All he said was: "Gentlemen, I'm a busy man, I have things to do. Go and get the requisite documents."

Sommer nonetheless is optimistic. "I'll get an *opholdstilladels!*" he says.

"What's that?"

"Shh! I'll tell you when I've got it!"

But the mood is generally optimistic. The conflict between the government and the Vatican seems to be intensifying. Air Marshall Balbo has been to see the Grand Master of the Knights of Malta, Prince Chigi. This in itself may appear to be an uninteresting piece of news, but the trained newspaper reader of the day looks beyond appearances: the event was reported only by the *Osservatore Romano,* while the Italian papers – I almost said "Aldo's papers" – did not cover it. On the other hand, they didn't *deny* it either, and therefore, according to the methodology of comparative newspaper studies, this means the following: the Grand Master summoned the knight Balbo to come and see him (since the system of honours now depends on your position in the Fascist Party and not the nobility of your ancestors, Balbo is at least a *balí* (knight) in the *gerarchia,* or peerage), and told him what he thinks of the whole mosque affair. Balbo is the governor of Libya, and therefore just the man whose word in Islamic affairs carries the necessary weight.

If the mosque doesn't get built, it would be a serious loss of prestige. The English have been storing up prestige for several centuries now, and can afford to lose a little of this precious stuff every now and again, when Hirohito's yellow-skinned soldiers strip-search an English subject at a Chinese port, say. But Italian prestige is all fresh, and has to be dealt with delicately, even despite Munich – or even because of it!

There is therefore no doubt that the mosque has to be built. Aldo reports the next day:

"We need a few days while the representatives arrive. It's all settled. We've even got the location. You know the Circus Maximus? Of course you do, it's at the foot of the Palatine Hill, where the exhibitions were. Opposite the Obelisk of Aksum and where the new building of the Ministry of African Affairs is going to be. That's where we're going to put it!"

It's not a bad place. Constantine's Arch opens from the Colosseum and the broad avenue takes you down past the ruins of the Emperors and the quiet gardens of the Caelius. Then it bends towards the Baths of Caracalla, which the visitors of the last century preferred to see by moonlight, and there – on the other side, will be the mosque, with its palm dates and arabesque fountain.

"We have to get a move on," Aldo says. "At any other time, we would have gone about it differently. The Minister for African Affairs and the Minister of Culture would have announced a tender. The opening of the exhibition of the entries for the tender is usually a minor ceremony in itself, the kind we send the King to open. Then there's the jury's decision, for which the entire art world turns out, or at least the plaster-mixing crowd of the Via Margutta. We know that they're a bunch of anti-fascists at heart, but for this sort of do, they'll don the black shirt. After all, we're their livelihood. Believe me, all those sculptors in plaster and bronze would have to go and be porters at the railway station if there weren't any more Duce statues. And after that, we'd have the laying of the foundation stone."

"But how will the mosque turn out if you don't do all that?"

"That doesn't matter. Just because we lay the foundation stone, it doesn't have to be a mosque – it could still become

anything else – a racing stables, say, or a lunatic asylum!"
Then he asks me rather confidentially, "Do you know any nice
famous Arabs?"

"Harun al-Rashid!"

"Out of the question! Rulers are out of the question. We
don't want to invite comparisons."

"I only know the doctors then. Avicenna!"

"What did he write?"

"The 'Canon'. One of the masterpieces of mediaeval medicine."

"Have you read it?"

"No."

"That's bad. Do you know if it contains any anti-fascist elements?"

"As far as I know, he writes mostly about laxatives. Castor
oil and so on…"

"Hmm…that's a sensitive subject. Well, I'll ask around. You
see, the University is going to erect a statue in the garden of
the mosque. If your Avicenna is ok, then it's enough if the
Faculty of Medicine sends someone. Would you like two com-
plementary tickets for the grandstand?"

"Thanks. I've never seen a foundation stone laid for a
mosque before."

In the days leading up to the event, we appear to live in the
world of the *Thousand and One Nights*. The papers report on
Baghdad and Basra. Famous Orientalists enlighten us on the
most beautiful *shura*s of the Koran. There's an Alladin's lamp
in the window of the Ministry of Propaganda. In my hungry
nights, I dream of mutton smothered in hot butter. It's hard
to find anything at all in the newspaper that is somehow not
related.

German troops have marched to the Demarcation Line.
The "little Maginot line" fell without a shot. New people appear on the scene: fathers of four pushing little carts, whole
families marching along the highway, like the wandering
avant-garde of a ragged, distant army. In the electricity station
that supplies the energy for the weapons factory in Pilsen, the
German occupiers appear and shut off the supply. An *"eintritt
verboten"* sign bars entry at the gate. These signs have carved

quite a place for themselves: they represent the new power, the way O.K. represents the US. The archives of Czech parishes are overrun with people suddenly researching their family trees. England is lending ten million pounds to what remains of the Czech government. The same people who have learnt the German expression "*eintritt verboten*" are now learning the English expression "conscience money."

How distant all that seems! Rome is preparing for the laying of the foundation stone.

"It's going to be a big occasion," Aldo tells me. "You should be glad you have a ticket. This time, we don't even have to order the postmen and the other municipal employees to attend…"

"Who?"

"Street-sweepers, dustmen, the people of the *netezza urbana*. There's eight thousand of them, if you count the bus conductors. They're the ones we call when we're not sure that the crowds will come of their own accord, or if we're sure they won't, like the last time, when Ribbentrop came to visit. But there'll be plenty of people there today. You can imagine how glad people are there won't be war. The Duce has never been so popular. Even the English are keen on him."

I try to find someone to come with me. Rosenwurz won't come because he's at home waiting for his affidavit. Pietro, the cobbler with the fine voice, says he's seen Aida so many times that he's not interested, and Attilio is studying. Among the "Geographical Society," only Péter Pogány is keen, the man I haven't even seen.

"Ok, let's go together."

Today, we sail smoothly over the otherwise dangerous waters of the Piazza Venezia. The secret policemen are busy guarding each individual tree on the Palatine, lining up from the Colosseum to the Ministry of African Affairs. It's a wonderful occasion to revise Attilio's physiognomy lesson. Péter Pogány is impressed by my knowledge: that one – yes, this one also, that one… maybe not. It's an advanced lesson today because, given the festive nature of the occasion, some of the secret policemen have brought their families with them.

But there's absolutely no doubt that the man taking the tickets on the grandstand is, in his day job, a secret policeman, and there's plenty of them scattered among the crowd, but we came on a ministerial ticket and whisper quietly in Hungarian.

From where we are, on the corner of the Palatine, we have a marvellous view over the entire scene. The parade will march under the Arch and then turn towards us at the Obelisk. The area of the Circus Maximus is closed off, and the crowd of several thousand is huddled on the hillock on the other side. The trams have stopped. The VIP stand is by the side of the Ministry of African Affairs, an enormous wood and papier-mache construction. It was erected in two days by *Cinecitta*, the big film studio, and from ten paces away the gigantic eagle, *fasces* and boat-like nose of its façade look like travertine marble. On film, in photos, it'll look like a fort cut out of solid rock. It's covered by a forest of flags: Italian, German, Egyptian, Abyssinian, fascist black triangles and the green flag of the Prophet. Crescents, swastikas, and fasces dance in the breeze, cleverly provided by the fans installed by the film studio (who've thought of everything). The clouds, though, are courtesy of St Peter.

The crowd on the VIP stand is beginning to gather. It's quite a collection of uniforms. Péter Pogány points out that the man I think is a general is actually a member of the Royal Guard, and that what I take to be a ship's captain is in fact a bureaucrat in the Ministry's latest uniform. There's seven or eight eagles per person, on buttons, hats, and lapels. It's a mistake to think that uniforms make people look uniform: everyone here is wearing a different uniform, and this makes for a colourful group. There's the black and white fascists, blue and white sailors, brown and blue and fish-grey Germans. Only a small minority wear clothes fit for European society.

"They're the Japanese," Peter tells me, and then points out others. "You see that man with the moustache? That's Count Ciano. No, not the Foreign Minister, his father. He's great. There's a law that anyone decorated with the Gold Medal of Military Valour doesn't have to pay tax. It was introduced back when the demobbed war heroes were given newspaper stands and ice-cream carts. The old man has the Gold Medal and is the president of two hundred and eighty companies.

You get it? See that little one? That's Starace, the Party Secretary. They say he's an idiot. They say that because he's been Party Secretary for eight years now. The Duce can't stomach anyone with an opinion for that long. People with opinions get fired."

"A changing of the guard?"

"Yes. You see, all the ministers here are lookouts. The dumbest one usually gets posted to the watchtower to shout '*halberdo!*' You don't need brains for that. The changing of the guard simply means that whatever the Minister knows, other people know too, or in other words, they tie a new ass to the same old cart."

The parade is approaching, the music gets louder. They're coming.

The parade is headed by Arab horsemen. They're a fine body of men, with beautiful horses. The film crews shoot them from stands, and lying on their bellies on the ground. Next come some heralds on horseback, then a troop of soldiers following a tattered, venerable Italian flag. The crowd raise their right hands to the sky.

Then come the fascist divisions. Every man jack of them is a standard-bearer. They're new men for new times. Whoever didn't get a flag has a heavy, gilded Roman-style pole (which will look bronze in the photos); and then behind the forest of flags and poles come more Arabs, this time infantry in white robes. There's an awful clanking that follows, of little tanks behind them, the torso of a man poking out of each. They look like motorised centaurs. Four huge ones follow behind, and while planes whirr overhead, more native infantry march past. It's hard to know whether they're erecting a mosque or a fort. Suddenly, a new cohort of Arab cavalry appears.

"Here comes the show!" Péter Pogány shouts.

"What?"

"This little game is an open secret, like the rest. There's a big ring road around the Palatine, and they send the troops round and round – the armies seem to get bigger with each circle. Huge armed forces march past the assembled military attaches, but there's only one fool enough to wire home ecstatically – and that's the Hungarian."

We watch the procession again. This time, though, it has a different ending. In a huge black car, standing with his manly chin jutting out towards the engine, his hands clasped to his waist, is the master of our destiny: the Duce. Behind him, mounted, are Marshalls Badoglio and Graziani, and a corps of bodyguards.

"The excitement was indescribable," the papers say whenever the Duce makes an appearance, and I shan't presume to describe the indescribable. Microphones capture and enhance the roar of the crowd.

The next scene, however, resembles a quadrille more than anything else. The Duce jumps elegantly out of the car onto the red carpet unrolled with superhuman speed at his feet. On one side, he's greeted by a group of Arabs accompanied for safety by two enormous blackshirts, and on the other by a clump of uniforms. As if ascending out of the ground itself, a bearded Arab mullah and his entourage appear before Mussolini. They all stop at exactly the same time.

Then comes the grand photo opportunity. Any event of historic significance can't be allowed to take place without one. After all, posterity will want to know how it all looked. All this is for the benefit of the textbooks of the future. Thus, the audience for these events grows *per omnia seacula saeculorum* – forever and ever. In mediaeval mystery plays, there existed such "invisible characters," who went about among the performers, moved things around, and shifted the scenery, while the audience took no notice of them. The Flemish Old Masters like to paint angels with two faces to symbolise the fact that although they were present at Christ's death, no-one saw them. Photographers are the invisible archangels of latter-day events.

The Duce never looks quite as much like himself in person as he does on photos. There, his freshly-shaved pate is that of an Emperor without his laurel wreath. His immobility becomes dignity. Care is taken to make sure that the people around him are wearing uniforms of a different colour than his. Today, he's the only one dressed in snow-white among all the black. He listens to the Arabs' laudatory speeches. He pays attention. One can see that, with an iron will, he's learnt

Arabic, too. After all, he was the only one at Munich who spoke German, French and English!

More dance-steps: the representative of the university presents the imam with a statue, one of the muftis gives the Duce a tiny carpet – evidently the miniature model of the Egyptian mosque carpet, and he, with a grand gesture, hands it on to the mullah. The German in the brown shirt brings a big book, and puts it down on the little table in front of the microphone.

"It's either *Mein Kampf* in Arabic, or the Koran in German," Péter Pogány surmises.

Then the Herr Gauleiter – or whatever one's supposed to call him – makes a short speech. In German, of course.

"My dear Arab friends," he says, "we understand each other. At this festive occasion, let me say only this, for you will all understand: Marx, Lenin, and Engels were not Arabs. The Führer's new Greater Germany looks to you with hope. So let us shout out loud: *Allah il Allah! Evviva il Duce! Heil Hitler! Sieg Heil, Sieg Heil, Sieg Heil!*

The photographers go hopping mad. Someone very obsequiously hands the Duce a hammer. The Duce, however, doesn't notice. He steps forward, draws the sword of Islam, and strikes the stone three times.

The applause and the shouting are truly indescribable. The Duce climbs the steps of the tribune with his famous bouncing walk, and goes straight to the prow of the fake ship. The Circus Maximus empties in a matter of moments, and the Arab cavalry enters the ring. They fly around the field with their billowing white cloaks, their guns rattling with joy-shots. The Duce once more becomes a statue of himself. The horses neigh, the film crews perform death-defying feats, running hither and thither in between the horses, the crowd chants "Du-ce, Du-ce", the secret policemen applaud, and the sun, which has seen similar things in this place before, as well as a wide variety of others, slips behind the trees of the Monteverde much like it tends to on historically less significant afternoons. The ceremony has come to an end.

The crowd rushes the newly-working tram like a troop of Arab horsemen. I amble home with Péter Pogány.

"This whole thing at Munich was nothing but pure poker," he complains. "I'll bet you all four of them were bluffing. And that's when the whole pot goes to the boldest liar. The problem is, they're bound to sit back down and have another game soon.

"What are your plans?"

"Out, out of here! But I haven't got my doctorate yet. I started late, I did a degree in Italian literature first. But I'll tell you about that another time."

"Guess what, Rosenwurz got a letter from America," Attilio tells me at home. "He got very excited, ran straight off. I think his visa might have arrived."

My stomach growls. I've been living on nothing but pizza too long.

"Is he coming back?"

"Maybe."

Aldo is also pleased. Everything went according to plan, even the sword-blows. Everything is ready for tomorrow: "The Duce has ordered that he be kept continuously informed of the progress of the works." The pictures will be in every newspaper in the world. The description of the event has already been typeset, yesterday. The Ministry of Propaganda has done its work perfectly. Aldo's boss is taking a few days of vacation.

Jurics is surprisingly well. I'm tired and hungry, and can't listen to his story, the point of which is always a giant hop! anyway. I give him his injection and go lie down on my bed. It's paid for for three more days.

Chapter X

Rosenwurz left me a little note before he left this morning: "I'm leaving for Naples on Wednesday at ten p.m. Come and see me three hours before. I have a lot to do until then. Please write down for me how to say in English: open your mouth, close your mouth, rinse."

It'll be nice for once to interrupt my diet of bread and water. I don't need pheasant – just a decent pastaciutta, with butter and parmesan, a good, man-sized steak, a big peach, fresh from the Frascati hills, and I swear that'll be enough encouragement and memory for two weeks. But for the moment, I'm hanging around the kitchen, in case Francesca happens to be making salad or peeling fruit. Or she might be buttering bread. When she does, she always politely says "*favorisca*", which means, help yourself. This is the same sort of polite phrase as the Portuguese have whenever they're eating in front of someone and they say "your Excellency's table is laid". One is not expected to respond. I know the rule, but in the guise of the innocent foreigner, I reply, "Oh, well, since you offered so kindly, yes I will have a little salad, thank you Francesca".

This time, I find Francesca and Miss Elsa working hard: they're trying to split an enormous hambone at the knee with a saw and what looks like a halberd. They're struggling. "Momento!" I say, remembering that it was Professor Eiselberg who taught me surgery. "Let me do it!" I borrow a razor blade from Attilio and apply myself to the task surgically. They started altogether in the wrong place. I find the *ligamentum laterale*, and make an incision above the meniscus. For a moment, I imagine that the patient's life depends on the skill of my knife. The joint is open now, and the two bones are connected only by a few interior ligaments. The operation is a success, and it only took a minute.

To this day, this has been my greatest triumph. It was a life-saving operation – it saved my life. In the afternoon, Francesca came to see me on behalf of the concierge – could I give her cousin an intravenous calcium injection? The doctor recommended a strengthening cure of twenty-four injections. He can pay one lira per injection. One lira means five slices of pizza. That's check to starvation.

"Fine. When do we start?"

"The day after tomorrow. Here's the address. Right next to the *Regina Coeli*."

Another patient! This is very reassuring. Otherwise, Jurics might well have outlived me – at least he eats. And who would have inherited his ten thousand lira then? On Wednesday, I no longer starve, but fast. I'm preparing myself for the feast.

Attilio and Pietro are invited too, but they're not excited by Rosenwurz's dinner. They always eat well, as if this were the most natural thing in the world.

That afternoon, around five, I am standing watching the town from the Obelisk next to the top of the Spanish steps. How beautiful it is, how calm! By six, the image of a steaming bowl of pasta has replaced the dome of St Peter's in my field of vision. What did Rosenwurz say? Seven? Yes, seven. I go home for seven sharp.

Rosenwurz embraces me.

"I'm leaving," he shouts, "Leaving! I had the ticket for the boat in twenty-four hours. Tomorrow morning, I'll be on a boat, and I'm so happy, I don't care if I'll be seasick! The Baltimore Castle sails from Naples. To America!" He turns serious for a moment. "America! It's so far. Another foreign language, and good dentists. Then there's the Klu-Klux-Klan, and the Mobsters!" but he quickly regains his good cheer. "America! It's a good country, built by Germans. All the breweries are German, all the sausages are German. They even have glee-clubs!" He looks at his watch. "My god, it's a quarter past seven! The train leaves at eight thirty!"

"But, Herr Rosenwurz…" I falter, "the dinner!"

"Oh the dinner! If you knew how sorry I was that we haven't got time for it! I've been thinking about it for weeks! How many times I've thought about us sitting down in a nice quiet little restaurant. I swear I'll regret not having had time for it all the way over to America. But then there's no such thing as an unmixed pleasure. *Des Lebens ungemischte Freude ward keinem Irdischen zu Teil!*" He jumps up and presses a wad of *Jüdisches Rundschau*s into my hand. They're all unopened. "I don't need that now," he says determinedly, "I'm going."

He shakes hands with everyone, and I can feel that he can no longer even see me. He's gone already, over on the other side, and he can feel the deep endless water between him and Pharaoh's army. In his excitement, his Italian leaves him, and he starts to hiccough. He grabs his little suitcase and goes. As he slams the door, like the true alumnus of the glee-clubs, he starts to sing. I can hear him from the street:

71

Es braust ein Ruf
Wie Donnerhall
Wie Schwertgeklirr
Und Wogenprall...

followed by the proud chorus –

Lieb Vaterland, magst ruhig sein.

And so it was that Herr Rosenwurz left for America. The same night, Jurics also left us, more quietly and for more distant shores.

When I went down the next morning with the needle, there were already candles burning around the bed. The inhabitants of the *pensione* – mostly artists, brought flowers, and the dutiful maid had her rosary in her clenched hands. Poor old Jurics! Why did he die?

I used to wander about that at autopsies, when I saw a ruined lung or cancerous liver – I can understand why they died, but why now? Why not yesterday, when he was just as ill? What happened in those last minutes, what was the actual cause of death?

What drove Jurics' heart in the last days? Why did he die just when I was in the greatest possible need of his ten thousand lira? The Circus has already phoned to say they'll take care of the funeral. The will is in the cupboard.

I thought I'd go and talk to Maxim, the Director of the Circus. As one of the witnesses to the will, I'll translate it for him. He'll be touched that Jurics thought of him first. I'm sure he'll help me get the money, too. The diamond ring is sparkling on Jurics' finger. That's Maxim's too, so let him come and remove it.

The Circus is far, right at the edge of town. I have no money for the bus and I have plenty of time to walk there, thinking over the new situation. I'm rich. I can now stay, and learn Italian. I'll be careful with my money, and have at least one day of *pizza* a week. From here, I'll go to France if things get worse. I could even lecture, if I spoke Italian. But first things first, I'm going to have a proper meal.

72

I find the circus. Its flags flutter merrily, as if its prize acrobat were still alive. The knife-thrower is practicing next to one
of the trailers – he's throwing long-bladed kitchen knives
around the painted outline of a woman. There's a stench of
lion around the big tent. I can hear an elephant trumpeting.

"Where's the Director?"

"In his trailer."

"I was Jurics' doctor."

"Oh, poor man. Come, I'll take you"

Maxim receives me sitting under his own portrait. He's so
proud, you'd think he founded a mosque each and every day.

"I've come about Mr. Jurics' will. I'm a witness. He's left his
villa in Budapest…"

"What did he leave?"

"That's not really important, but he did leave a hundred
thousand lira to the circus staff!" Maxim is looking at me now
with an offended air. I can see he's upset that Jurics didn't
leave the bulk of his fortune to him personally.

"And he left you, personally, his platinum and diamond
ring!"

At this, the Director sprang up dramatically:

"Knock it off, what do you think this is, a circus? Some of us
have work to do!"

"But the ring!"

Maxim yanks open a drawer irritably, pulls out a bag and
empties it on the desk. Out pour hundreds of diamond rings,
all engraved "Circ. Maxim."

"That ring?" he asks. But, having seen my face when he
does, he adds with a little more kindness, "I bought two thousand of them in Brussels. We raffle one off at every show. It's
paste and glass. They're nice, people get very excited over
them." He sweeps the precious hoard back into its bag, and
since I still haven't said a word, he says, "Jurics' diamond. He
was a hell of a character, the old man! Did he tell you he was
an acrobat? That was his favourite story. He was a circus assistant with the Romanos-Viofranc lot. Ten years ago, we both
happened to arrive in Genoa at the same time, we were going
on to Turin. I said to Romanos, 'Do you have anyone who
speaks German? We bought an elephant from Hagenbeck in

Hamburg (this elephant). Someone has to go and fetch it'. So Romanos said 'There's Jurics. He can speak German, Slovak, French. He's a hell of an old crook, but you could give him a try'. The money was already in Hamburg, so I decided to try Jurics. Either he'd bring the elephant, or he wouldn't. Fact is, he never did steal the elephant, so we kept him on too."

I make one more desperate attempt. "But his daughter! His successful daughter!"

"Yes, quite right. She married the porter at the Hotel Etoile in Marseilles. Nice lady, works there too. We'll let her know."

I daren't ask any more questions. Except one:

"I was Jurics' doctor. My fees…"

But Maxim is once more the cool dictator. "I'm sorry. That's not our affair. Jurics hasn't worked for six months, but we kept him on at full pay. He said he had to go see a professor once, we even paid for that. But you must understand that in today's straitened circumstances, we can't pay for everything!"

He looks me over once more and then asks, "Would you like a free ticket to tonight's show?"

"I can't tonight."

"You can come whenever, Sundays and holidays excepted."

"Tomorrow, then?"

"As you please."

I wandered out. The old clown… the inheritance… hop!… hop! a kitchen knife slams into the wall an inch away from my nose.

"The exit's that way!"

I find it at last. I spend my first night without shelter under the tent of Maxim's Circus.

Chapter XI

My little suitcase has stayed at Miss Elsa's, she'll keep it for me as long as I like. I can come and see the boys, too, and can keep Francesca company in the kitchen – but my room has already been let to an older man who only comes home to sleep, and locks it by day. I stare at its door like Adam outside the gates of Paradise.

In many countries, there's a compulsory period of service in the army. And in Burma, every man must spend time – days or years – in a monastery. Ernő Szép says in *Purple Blossoms* that if the world really must contain Jews, then everyone should spend six months as a Semite. I would say that everyone pass their homelessness exam.

Not so much to understand the emotional state of the homeless person, which they would quickly forget anyway. Everyone should live on the streets for a few weeks at some point in order to teach them to love their bed for the rest of their lives.

It's not easy, becoming homeless. Even people really down on their luck, incompetents, drunks, tend to find some shack, a sack of straw. But a world war will do it. In peacetime, even former prisoners and wanderers will find a bed for the night, but the events that turn your life upside down also turn you out of your bed.

And it's not easy, getting out of homelessness. The difference between someone with a bed and without is much greater than the difference between someone with a bed and someone who owns their own room. That is a social difference. Homelessness is a chronic illness.

It wouldn't be so hard to be homeless – if it weren't for the nights! I wander the city in my new guise, as if it were a completely different city from yesterday's Rome. Rosenwurz is gone, the sunken-eyed girl has aged, Jurics is dead – how much loss I've already endured! My clothes leave me too, "like rats do a sinking ship," I think to myself. My shirts were the first to go, with the help of the good lady who scrubs the stairs in the Street of Lives (or Screws). She once mentioned that her husband had ulcers on his feet. I went to see him, treated him, bandaged him, and since they didn't have any money, we agreed that she would do my washing. And since she couldn't let herself work for free either, I now only have two shirts left – one on my back, and the other in my suitcase-cum-house. I don't even know her name, I used just to call her *Piedisporchi* (Filthyfeet). She rather astutely deduced that I would no longer need my pyjamas, either. Every time I look down at my knees, I think of Mussolini's stomach lining. There remains now only a hair's breadth to separate the cobblestones from the soles of my feet. Only my black overcoat is faithful, and keeps me warm in the October nights.

I don't have anywhere to live, but I do have a job: the daily injections. The concierge's cousin started his cure on time. It's my good fortune that calcium is so much in vogue. A mediocre doctor could make quite a decent living from intravenous injections of calcium. A few hundred thousand people were happy in the belief that calcium makes you younger, gives you an appetite and helps you keep up your weight. I have no idea how they managed to convince them of this, but this miracle drug really was capable of making patients out of perfectly healthy people for a few weeks. Its glorious reign lasted right up until the vitamin revolution came along and swept it from the corridors of power. Before that, the boiling of the syringe, the tiny drop of blood sucked back through the needle, and the warm glow that followed the injection were perfectly enough to satisfy the good people who were so adamant about making sacrifices for their health.

My patient lives next door to the prison dedicated to the Heavenly Queen because he's a gaoler by profession. His window opens onto the narrow little street that they call the Street of the Knife, *Via del Coltello*, and surely not without reason. The prisoners' relatives, who bring them food in black bags twice a week know this ancient, steep divide well, which leads them from the Gianicolo to the Tiber.

The gaoler is a remarkably nice man, with a name so complicated to pronounce that I just call him Mr. Key. His ivory-haired mother may well have known the prison in its original incarnation, when (like so many other public buildings in Rome), it bore its name with reason, since it was a nunnery. Mr. Key comes home from work at four p.m., and I am already there. I've realised that with some sort of excuse, I can turn up as early as two ("oh, I had something to do in the neighbourhood at noon, and it's really not worth going all the way home"). The mother will say, "Come in and wait, *dottore*, my son will be home presently", and then disappear into the kitchen, where like some ancient Vestal virgin she keeps the charcoal fire going. The fan with the big feathers moves as if automatically in her hand, for hours, ceaselessly. I try it too, but get tired after only a couple of minutes. There is an eternal pot of *minestra* simmering on the stove, very occasionally replaced by a large tin mug of coffee. I can lie down on the sofa in the living room, and can have a delicious little nap. They say that Napoleon could go to sleep at any time – and in this one respect I very much resembled the unfortunate Corsican at the time. Fading into the maroon of the sofa and the half-light of the room, I left the world of mosques and consulates happily behind. My patient rings at four – or sometimes even at five.

We boil the needle on the charcoal fire. I listen to Mr. Key's office gossip refreshed from my sleep.

"It's not like it used to be. There's lots of work, no shortage of that. They've even turned the Popes' old prison, which has been a museum of criminology for fifty years, back into a prison. But the crowd inside now are a refined lot. You can't imagine the sort of crooks we had before! They had saws hidden everywhere, and wouldn't stop knifing each other. But our guests now (Mr. Key refers to his prisoners by this term) are real gentlemen. You can listen to some of them for hours. It's a real pleasure going to work in the morning now, chatting to some of them. It's a shame that there's such overcrowding that no-one stays very long. They get taken off to Civitavecchia, Ponza, the islands. But maybe it'll get better when they build the new modern prison outside the city.

"Have they laid the foundation stone yet?" I ask, like someone who knows how these things go.

"It's enough to have a resolution from the special court," Mr Key assures me.

"Are they strict?"

"I know a judge, a good man, decent man, started work last year and he's already handed down twenty thousand years' worth of incarceration. Since the sanctions and the war in Abyssinia, politicals are getting ten or twenty years like thieves used to get their six months, before."

Best to stay on good terms with my patient, after all – who knows when he might not become my landlord?

From there, I walk back to my former paradise. Aldo comes home around this time, and he brings the day's papers with him. If I got sad in the *Via del Coltello*, I can cheer myself up a bit. Here, *tout va bien dans le meilleur des mondes* (all is well in this best of possible worlds). A new campaign has begun – this time, with chemists taking the place of Arabs. The campaign is autarchy.

The Ministry of Propaganda has excelled itself once again. The great move towards self-sufficiency has begun, which will make Italy independent of foreign raw materials. The country gets progressively stronger as it renounces the unnecessary goods peddled by the plutocracies. There, for starters, is the matter of iron girders. Why buy iron, when there's so much of it about? Old metal fences, derelict bridges are an excellent source of iron. The wasteful old liberal regimes even put the Pantheon in a cage. But fascism will re-conquer this valuable metal.

One of the beauties of this campaign is that it's open to interpretation. Italy wants war. Not at all! Italy is working towards peaceful progress, trying to make the capitalist competition for raw materials – a cause of so much conflict – a thing of the past. Italy is afraid of war. Not in the least! Autarchy will help the country be self-sufficient in the event of a blockade.

Francesca has a new respect for me since I operated on the ham, and usually finds me a little leftover cold stew. It's also lucky for me that Italians don't like to eat the inside of the bread. They eat the crust and leave the rest. Francesca thinks of me and collects what's left on the plates at lunch.

My next stop is the Greco. It's good to have a goal in mind, to walk with purpose, as if I had some important thing to do. The "Geographical Society" is in session, only Bakó is frequently absent – his wife doesn't like it if he's out in the evenings. Sommer is kept away by the struggle for autarchy. This time, he too has joined the fight – he's offered to make a whole set of new dentures for the mother-in-law of the concierge of a certain building, if that concierge were to donate that building's metal railings to the national cause. The deal having been struck, the concierge put up a notice in the house to the effect that any tenants opposing the donation of the grilles in the staircase to the national cause should present themselves to him and explain their reasons. As none of the tenants was fool enough to do *that,* the grilles were removed. Since their removal, the concierge's mother-in-law is back on a solid diet, and Sommer arrives – if he comes at all – later than usual and blushing slightly.

At midnight, the Greco closes, and this is the saddest moment of my day. I start walking somewhere. I peruse the map of the city in my head – isn't there a quiet place to rest anywhere on there? Well, there's the cemetery. I could, as the Romans say, go and sleep "under the tall trees". But I can't even afford the rope. And when I do have the two lira necessary for the rope, I am in my right mind again – I buy *pastasciutta.* The fact is, I have to go somewhere, I can't just sit down on the edge of the pavement. Patrols with a policeman and two fascist militiamen criss-cross the city; I'd best be careful.

When I have half a lira, I can get the tram. There are two lines that run right around Rome. The trams run round and round, like an old beggarwoman's fingers on her rosary. You can doze nicely off and let the tram shake and carry you as you go round the city walls. When it rains, I bless the engineer that made this perpetual motion machine. If I don't have the necessary capital for the tram, I can go out to the Via Flaminio – there's a tall, clay hill on one side of it. Wise people with foresight have cut holes into it, and these are cosy and warm, but make your clothes dirty. You have to take newspaper, if you can find any. Sometimes, the holes are already occupied – there are other homeless people beside me, some with more experience. The Capitoline Hill isn't bad, either. One of Rome's ancient and beautiful streets, the Via Rupe Tarpea, has been sentenced to death. They want to make the sacred hill into a garden and memorial. They've already demolished some of the houses, and the rest look out in a state of semi-ruin over the thick scrub of the Palatine. These empty houses still have rooms, and in one of them I even found an old, comfortable leather armchair. The sun rises here also.

The best solution of course is the all-night restaurant – but that requires money, at least two lira. You can get by with a plate of soup from midnight to three a.m., and from three to five you can think about the political situation, and at five they open the churches. If only they'd built the mosque! The house of Allah is open night and day, and King Fuad's carpet is bound to be soft and thick. The pews of the churches are hard, and it's hard to sleep kneeling with your head bowed. I like the German church, the Santa Maria dell'Anima. They always open on time and there are never any visitors. The gloom inside only gets deeper with the lighting of the candles. I stretch out quietly on the farthermost bench. Once – just once – I snuck into the confession booth. I woke to a soft woman's voice on the other side of the grille. It was speaking Italian, very quietly. I coughed a little now and then, my heart was beating fast, I could hardly wait for her to finish. If someone should find me... the priest himself, perhaps... what could this creature have done that she be kneeling here at five in the morning, clouding the grille with the breath of her sin? There's silence for a moment, her voice breaks off.

"Absolvo te, absolve te" I almost shout in fear.

I hear her leave. I may even have helped her. But I never again dared go back to the Anima. Instead, I go to the French church for the early mass. This is where Monsignor Cabillaud, who until then I'd only met in the café, catches me one morning. We were both a little surprised.

"It's nice that you come so early to mass!"

I have no reason to lie to him. "Monsignor, I have not come for the mass. I lost my faith a long time ago. I don't even know what it's good for, any more."

The old *abbé* is too wise to try to convince me, or convert me. He looks past me, searching for something very distant with his eyes.

"Faith is good... when one gets some terrible piece of news. Then, it's good to have faith, to be able to cling to something eternal, something sacred. Faith is good in times of trouble." He looks at me as if blessing me.

At six, the bakers open. The pizza is fresh and hot, and the cold water of the fountains washes off the traces of the night. If I have saved Mr Key's lira, if Francesca has not forgotten the insides of the bread that is, I can go to a little barbershop behind the Piazza Navona. This is the best part of my day.

The warm water gushes, the barber works away like a sculptor tracing from the shapeless foam the old contours of my face, as if with a chisel. The most glorious bit is when I get to bury my face in the towel.

Then I can choose – either I can go see Miss Elsa, and go lie down on Aldo or Attilio's bed. If I've had some sleep, I can go sit in the Greco, where only Lewis is holding the fort this early. We talk a little.

"The white rose!" the poet says.

I don't fully understand what's white, and what's eternal, the rose or the eagle. I'd like him to repeat his immortal line, but I have to give up this ambition as many more before me. After all, he's right: everybody knows that Homer wrote the *Iliad*, and Dante the *Inferno*. But who reads them? And who dares question the greatness of their authors? A name, and a title – that's glory. A title will last forever!

"The rose that never dies!"

I walk over to Mr. Key's for two o'clock – his mother often gives me a hot cup of milky malt coffee. There is no better, sweeter drink in the world than this. There is an eternal harmony between the human body and the warm, sweet, fragrant milk. The burnt taste of the coffee lends an unusual charm to this short, inner celebration, and then the warm embrace of the red sofa gathers me in.

The days flow into each other. In the place of black nights and sunny mornings, looking back, I see a grey cloud. The circular tram rocks me to sleep, I fall upon the steaming malt coffee greedily, and I'm never fully awake. Sometimes, I long for that red sofa as an amorous student does for his lover's bed. Like the rich, and those who live on solid ground, I can no longer see oncoming dangers, either. Just once, once, I'd like to sleep in a bed!

I count the days in Mr. Key's supply of calcium. There's ten doses left, then five. Then Key buys another course, because he says the calcium is doing him good – but I don't know how many injections there are in the new course, and so I lose my calendar.

There's a funny substance in the human liver, glycogen, discovered by Claude Bernard, one of the great physiologists of the 19th century. When the body needs it, it can make sugar quickly and easily from this little molecule. Muscles run on sugar. It was László Németh who first came up with the idea of emotional glycogen: those dear, sweet thoughts from which the tortured body makes sugar in times of hunger and sleeplessness. If I ask myself what kept the strength in me, other than the sheer will to live, I have to say it was my emotional glycogen. If I had been a writer or a poet, I could have convinced myself that this was that misery which ancient and distinguished professors have identified as necessary parts of the experience that form the poet's voice. Sadly, I am not an artist, and besides, it's my firm belief that this idea was dreamt up by heartless loansharks to ease their conscience as they watch people with talent starve. *"Oh, he'd never have written his 'De Profundis' if we'd fed him!"*

I have much to thank Sándor Török for. It was he who noted and described the "obliging miracle," that mysterious mechanism which kicks in just before the last of your strength leaves you, just before the last piece of bread. Mentally, I salute Sándor Török, while physically, I am all about proving the truth of his idea. Yes, it's true: if you drop a man in a foreign city where he can barely even speak the language, he can rely on the obliging miracle, because it will come. Yes, it's difficult to stay well-fed, yes it's very difficult to find somewhere to sleep, but it's even more difficult to starve to death. There are special places, ringed with barbed wire, for that in Europe.

I have an obliging miracle to thank for the unexpected luxury of the barber and the all-night restaurant, a hot bath and sweet coffee. One evening, I found ten lira in the Piazza di Spagna. Emboldened, and despite my best intentions, I run to the first restaurant. Someone calls my name – three doctor friends of mine from Vienna, former students from the Physiological Institute, say hello.

"Are you on holiday too?"

"Yes, that's right. "

"We've been sent by the German government to study tropical diseases. We've signed on to go and spend five years in the Congo or German South Africa afterwards. We were in

Brussels first, and learned a lot. There's not much to learn here, the facilities are so primitive! So we've decided to do some sightseeing. We've got three thousand lira a month".

"Between you?"

"No, each".

It's nice to have an expansionist Führer to pay one's bills...

They pay for my dinner, I stay with them. I'm more used to the long nights than my happy debauchees. I walk them back to their hotel.

"It's a long way home. Could I stay on your couch?"

"Yes, of course, be my guest".

I show them round Rome, my adopted city, for three days. They are most interested by the columns of Bernini's Tabernacle and the mysterious motifs decorating the marble. The casual observer will see only a shield covered in bees and a grotesque baroque monster, but the doctor will notice what the mischievous sculptor hid within the mass of decorations – a realistic and raw depiction of childbirth. The face of a young woman in her labour pains is visible above the shield, or relaxed in between contractions, and by the eighth relief, she's joined by the happy baby. The baroque monster is the working flesh, the body opening itself...the altar where only the heir of Peter can say mass, is surrounded by an artistic representation of one of the most traumatic human experiences.

We go round the galleries, the museums, the wine bars. They remind me that there's other things in the world, too:

"Next year, we'll have our colonies. Did you know that in Berlin alone fifty thousand people enrolled for a course in Swahili? We'll get triple pay in Africa!"

"Will there be war?"

They laugh. "No, it'll be just like now. The Führer will pick the right moment. The French? They won't fight. *Mourir pour Congo*? Die for Congo? The democracies are just pleased that we don't have any more territorial claims in Europe. They've even accepted all this officially."

"One thing's for sure", continues Pepi Klausner. "The Blacks won't be allowed in the cinemas and the nightclubs."

"*Verboten*," I shrug.

I like doctors who are optimistic. I spend three well-fed days with them, I hardly have time for Mr. Key. "See you in Africa!" they say happily in parting, and I reply no less happily that when I do, I'll give them back all the small change they lent me.

It's also thanks to an obliging miracle that Bakó invites me to his place just when the rain starts. It's a real African rain, it soaks you to the skin, a tropical rain that the Romans call *sgrullone.*

Bakó's wife is Italian. They live between the railway and the University, because Bakó works at the clinic. Since the Rosenwurz debacle, I'm suspicious of dinner invitations, and just to be sure, I go pick up the insides of the bread after I've seen Mr. Key. From there, I walk nice and slowly up to the railway, speeding up only where my path approaches the invisible frontiers of the secret policemen.

She's the first Italian woman who shakes my hand. What an extraordinary thing the female hand is! Antaeus regained his strength when he touched mother Earth. We are all like Antaeus – from time to time, we need to touch a woman's hand.

A woman whose language you don't understand can be intimidating. Even a woman with whom you're able to talk in earnest, a woman with whom you may spend years in the same room, has enough secrets. Someone you don't even know how to say "that was nice" to when they give you a hug is very scary. I've not been here long enough, I think all Italian women are the same. I'm unable – and too sleepy to boot – to find a face in which I think I can see someone who thinks the same as me. I do understand a few things – Francesca revealed some things despite her iron mask – but before Bakó's wife, even my slender vocabulary slips away. Thankfully, all Italians start the conversation the same way.

"How long have you been in Rome? Do you like Italy?" And by now, I can expect a little bit of praise: "Your Italian's pretty good."

"Come," says Bakó. "Come to my room. My wife will put on the pasta."

I learn something new. Here, people don't wait for guests with a meal that's almost ready, but with boiling water. They don't trust people to be on time – and rightly so, because a housewife's worst nightmare is soggy, soft macaroni. You can't just arrive here, and move straight to the dinner table.

Bakó has books! Books of his own. I'd forgotten that anyone could have anything more than a bed. From afar, I spot Kraepelin's '30 Lectures' and Genil-Perrin's book on paranoia. He shows them to me with a collector's pride.

"Have you read this one? Nora Waln – 'Reaching for the Stars.'

"No, what's it about?"

Bakó doesn't reply at once, but starts explaining with an expansive gesture: "Do you know what a good book is? A good book is one that – be it in two lines or two hundred pages – fixes an image, or a phrase, in you that you can't ever forget from then on. One that adds a new string to the bow of your memory, and if you pluck that string in ten years time, it still sounds the same. This woman, an American Quaker, gives an image of the Germans and of the Gestapo that you'll never forget!"

He leafs through the book and starts to read: "'Some rabbits are peacefully at breakfast in the field. Suddenly, a fox jumps out of the forest. The rabbits scatter – but one or two are caught – the fox drags them off. Then the rabbits return, and the scene is just as peaceful as before...' That's what I'm talking about!" Bakó shouts, "That's conscience! That's the peace that the traveller sees and describes. Their heroes, their parades! This Nora is a visionary, she's seen them for what they really are. That? That's Mowrer's *Germany Puts the Clock Back.* It's three hundred pages, and it's worth reading. There's this beautiful symbolic scene, which says more than a whole library full of books on psychology: 'The German students in their coloured hats and with colourful flags parade in front of the university in Berlin, shouting rhythmically'. Do you know what they're shouting? *Wir scheissen auf die Freiheit* ['We shit on freedom'], and I can well imagine they pronounced it syllable by syllable. There's seventy million people's state of mind in seven syllables for you. That? You should read that too. Borghese's *Sawdust Caesar*, it's an excellent book, and it'll be especially good for you, what with not

85

really knowing the country yet. It's got two good sentences of its own – don't laugh, be grateful if a book doesn't take up your time without giving you something worthwhile – 'Italy did not annex Fiume, rather it was D'Annunzio's operetta-world that annexed Italy', and 'Fascism is not revolution, but involution'. Did you know that it was D'Annunzio that came up with all this? He meant it as a joke, because he was an imaginative thinker – the black shirts, the Roman salute, the centurions and consuls, the '*eia-eia alala*' and all the rest of this nonsense. People laughed at the little tasselled hats, but the second they put them on they stopped laughing. Revolution? One after the other they did away with all the accomplishments of liberal Italy: voting, the freedom of association, trade unions. Involution! That's why Borghese lives in America now. This is Vergin's book – *Subconscious Europe*. Read it – he makes his point wonderfully. He says that Catholic Spain, France, and Italy live under the pressure of incense and taboo, that every effort is threatened by perpetual Reaction, and that's why it's precisely here that there are these incredible outpourings and bloody orgies. The subconscious of the Scandinavian countries is not in such an explosive state... Rauschnigg – *Gesprachte mit Hitler*. A clever book. Hitler may even have said all those things, but there's only one sentence of this book too that is really alive: 'Hitler, in his anger, throws himself to the floor'. This is what started that story about him eating carpets, which hurt Hitler more than anything else... Why are *Mein Kampf* and *Don Quixote* next to each other? Think about it, if that crazy Spaniard had written his memoirs, what do you think he would have called them? *Mi batalla!* And he would have been right, too. All these paranoiacs are so alike! Cervantes writes, 'He added the name of La Mancha to his own, because he was proud of his native land, and considered it a special honour to have been born there...' And Hitler? He starts off by thanking Fate for having been born in Braunau..."

"I'm surprised the fascists even let these books into the country."

"In that respect they're better than the Germans. *Diktatur gemildert durch Schlamperei* [Their disorganisation makes their dictatorship more bearable]. That's what they used to say about Metternich. But there's another thing – it isn't worth banning a book for the benefit of the handful of people here who read English and French. It's another matter altogether if the book is translated. But even so, quite a lot slips through the nets of the Ministry of Propaganda – they only live and work for the readers of the papers, anyway. Someone who'll sit down and read a book, a proper book, with a mind and a soul, is never going to be a happy part of the militia anyway, don't you see?"

The pasta's ready, we move to table. Oh, to be eating sitting down, off plates and a tablecloth!

"You should get married," Bakó advises me. "There's no better wife than the Italian. Of course, she's jealous, but that's ok, and you can hardly fault her for that. When she was a girl, she was jealously guarded – as an adult, it is she who guards jealously. This is her task, her life. The bigger problem is that in the morning, she breaks the bread into the coffee, like a toothless old woman. There's absolutely nothing you can do about it. I've stopped having breakfast."

I didn't know Bakó had a son, but the boy is nearly three years old.

"My wife spoils him," Bakó tells me, "there's nothing doing. Italian women are too good to their children. Here, every little brat is a *povero tesoro* [poor darling]." Then he adds angrily, "Mussolini started off as a *povero tesoro* too!"

After dinner – after that magical dinner! – we go back to the library. I'm surprised by the long list of Hungarian authors.

"Yes, they're all translated. That is, all our second-rate literature, all the penny dreadfuls and so on. Don't bother with them, most of the translations are appalling. I think it was one of the typists at the Embassy and a customs officer who translated Babits' *The Nightmare* to death. The publishers pay badly, and so the translators translate badly, and so the publishers pay badly. It's a vicious circle and there's no way out. But fascism will not abide home-grown literature that deals with contemporary problems. The only thing you can write here is fairytales or songs of praise. No wonder people are reading Zilahy, Körmendi, Földi and Márai instead."

"Yes, no-one misses the point quite as elegantly as Márai."

"You can read one book by him. But two is already too many."

Bakó is not a psychologist for nothing:

"Where are you living?" he suddenly asks me. I don't know what to tell him: the tram, the red sofa...

"I'm just in between places," I reply. "For just a few days – it wasn't worth..."

"Stay here tonight," he says, and not even having the strength to politely refuse, he starts arranging things for me. I sleep in a bed, a real bed. Maybe one day one of the truly great writers will succeed in describing what a mattress, a pillow and a blanket really mean – but I have no metaphors, my words desert me.

In the morning, Bakó tells me to come back that evening. The temptation is great; I go back. It's a funny thing, being well-rested. You see further, you're more sure of yourself, and your thoughts don't stop when the grey cloud invades your mind. I give the red sofa a look of arrogant pride. What a battered old thing it is! How much more beautiful my bed is!

But on the third night, I suddenly feel that it isn't mine at all. I'm not dulled into unconsciousness by the need to sleep, I realise that I'm a guest. More than a guest: a burden. I read once that in China, no-one dares save someone who's drowning, because the person rescued then has the right to expect his rescuer to support him, seeing as he gave him life, like a sort of second father. And if the rescuer refuses, the soaking Chinaman will stand on the street corner and shout: *Look at that degenerate! He pulled me out of the water but refuses to support me!*

I can feel that Bakó and his wife can't throw me out, can't ask me to go. But I don't want to be the good doctor's soaking Chinaman.

I write a little note, "I've found a room, thank you both for your hospitality, I'll be in touch soon," give the bookshelves one last caress, and go.

It's at midnight that night, in front of the Greco, that I regret my noble act. But it's too late now, and so on to the tram.

Chapter XII

I'm curious how long I can live like this. I'd like to know how far obliging miracles will carry one. There's four or five injections left in Mr. Key's box.

It's going to be hard without the sofa. And I'm quite close to Key now, too. He's noticed that my soles have holes in them, and quite without prompting says, "Come by tomorrow at two, and I'll take the shoes over to get resoled".

"But I can't afford a cobbler!"

"Oh, these cobblers work for free."

The next day, he takes my shoes – and their holes – over to the Heavenly Queen. As well as cobblers, they have carpentry, basket-weaving and paper-cone making workshops, too. And while a notorious pickpocket nails the Italian state's leather onto the bottom of my shoes, Key's mother makes malted coffee. Fundamentally, I can say that I've been lucky – when it rains, most of the human race gets wet feet. But I will once again be one of the illustrious minority for whom that is not so.

"I'm happy to help," says Key. "You can see that even our profession has its perks. But believe me, it has its drawbacks. Our guests are mostly sad, and quite often in a bad mood. It's hard to cheer them up. They can spend months, sometimes years, waiting for their trial. I often think 'what a marvellous man he must be, free,' and many people tell me to come and visit them when they get out. I did go, once or twice, but they get scared when they see me, it makes them remember the lice. Everybody likes the postman,' he adds sadly.

I swore that I'd like to sleep in a bed "just once more," but I lied. I want to sleep in a bed every night – or at least, under a roof. I go and see how the mosque is getting on. In Abyssinia, they built bridges, roads and tunnels in a matter of weeks!

The foundation stone is still there. I walk around it. If I had a sword, I could strike it, but it's no good for sleeping on. I blame Aldo for this delay.

"We did our job," he says. "The mosque is finished."

I assure him that he's mistaken.

"You're too materialistic," he tells me, "a man of the past. Did you know that a model of the mosque is displayed in four hundred Arab cities? Every newspaper in the world wrote about the laying of the foundation stone. Since the Duce struck that stone with his sword, the mosque has become a reality – in the intellectual sphere."

He continues philosophically, not unlike Bakó himself:

"Reality is what everyone knows, and believes to be true. *Deus cogitatur, ergo est* [God exists, because he exists in my thought]. One of our philosophers, who you won't know, said, 'What is not written down has not been thought of. What is not printed, is not written'. The mosque exists in our thinking and in writing. It's real even for the Arabs of the Gulf of Bahrain. It is already a symbol, already a victory. I assure you that no-one wanted, and no-one can want, anything more. After all, you're not going to go and see for yourself if the pyramids are really there in the desert."

"But if someone..."

"If that someone isn't the Minister for Propaganda, then his objections are in vain. I assure you that so far as Italy, Germany, Hungary, and Albania are concerned, the mosque exists. What doesn't exist is whatever we don't consecrate in newsprint."

"What's that?"

"Suicide, for one. In the last fifteen years in this happy country, not a single person has thought of doing away with themselves. It doesn't exist. Crime? Look at the American papers, they're full of crime. But we've got nicer stories, we don't want to raise a bunch of little Dillingers. Unhappy marriages? Divorce? No such thing. It doesn't get a word of newsprint. And without that, even reality is just a dream. And besides, the Church has acknowledged that ours is the cleanest press in the world. Financial scandals, embezzlement of public funds, corruption... all that doesn't exist."

Aldo switches his role from teacher to prophet:

"We live for posterity. We'll leave behind a clear, shiny image of ourselves. For now, people are whispering, they know better than the papers, but put something in writing, print it, and in five hundred or a thousand years... but what am I saying, in ten years, it's a historical document! You can't see the mosque, but the historians will see it, as the Bedouins have done. We will bear witness to our age. But on another note, there's a German trio playing somewhere near here tomorrow. It's old music, not for me. Do you want my ticket?"

"Is it harpsichord music?"

"I think so."

"Yes, go on, give me your ticket, and I'll believe in your mosque. Can I lie down on your bed?"

"Sure, you can stay till midnight, I'll be home late tonight."

Sleep before midnight is the best. I get on the tram refreshed.

It's the Freiburg Chamber Trio that's playing; Telemann, Bach, Haydn... old music, old Germany, old world. But it was worth living in it nonetheless – how beautifully the harpsichord sounds for Johann Sebastian Bach!

The three musicians bowed after the final note like wooden dolls broken in half at the midriff, and disappeared. The harpsichord stayed on the stage. I can't resist, the keys are calling me, I go sit down in front of them. It takes me a minute to get used to the keys, a little too light, and then – my body produces sugar from my emotional glycogen. Lalo, Lully... those sweet, light, melancholy and crystal clear Frenchmen!

I thought I was alone, but I was mistaken. A gentleman waits for me to finish, and then very simply asks:

"Would you have time to play with me sometimes?"

"Absolutely."

"Tomorrow night at eight?"

"Absolutely."

He gives me his card, we say goodnight, he leaves.

He seems to be Spanish: Don Agesilao Anguillara. Where does he live? Oh, I'll find it somehow. I'd like to know, though, what time the Spanish usually have dinner. I'm afraid it might be seven – I hope it's more like quarter past eight. Maybe he's the man the gypsywoman was thinking of.

It would be nice to go back to the Bakós'. I feel I've served my time, I wait for Fate to deliver me a new task. It's cold. The railway station waiting room isn't heated, but there's plenty of people and they help warm it up. At midnight, I can choose between the lukewarm but loud waiting room and the quiet

91

but growing cold outside. In any case, I'll wait and see what Don Agesilao brings into my life.

I delay the barber until the evening, and brazenly leave it till next time to pay. Worst comes to the worst, I'll never go back to the area. My standards are slipping.

There's a labyrinthine warren of small streets that lead from the *Gesú*, the Jesuits' jewelbox church, to the Amphitheatre of Marcellus and the old Ghetto. Rich, ancient palaces, monasteries; the mediaeval houses squeezed in between them hardly leave space for the narrow alleys that traverse them, so that you breathe a small sigh of relief when you reach the little square in the middle of all this. There's a fountain playing in the centre, and my rendezvous is in the palace overlooking it.

I ring the bell and wait. How many friendly doors I've known! There were ones I even had keys to. Then, there was one I knew, which if I knocked three times, would open slowly, carefully. But how cold and forbidding an unknown door can be.

A concierge opens the door. I tell him my name. He makes me wait a little, then hands me over into the care of a butler. Being so sleepy makes me incurious. I simply wait to see what happens next. The worst that can happen is that there won't be any dinner. At least the gentleman doesn't require a visa for my visit. From one of the walls, a bearded knight in armour and ruff looks down on me – you can tell he's pretty ancient. I suddenly remember that priests and princes also sometimes use the honorific 'Don'. The man I met certainly wasn't a priest... The butler hands me over to yet another gentleman, and by now my curiosity is aroused. He opens the door before me and vanishes.

"Good evening," says the man I took for a Spaniard.

The room is a huge library, with age-old furniture, a piano, and Oh! a little table already laid. It's a good thing that my trousers still have a little weave at the knees.

After a few sentences the Don – or prince – asks me:

"Would you rather we spoke English?"

"Oh yes."

Conversation becomes easier. If my host didn't occasionally mispronounce 'only' as 'hoanely', I would have thought him a native Brit. As it is, there can be no doubt that he was at university in England. This somewhat reassures me regarding my appearance. Perhaps he thinks I go around dressed like this merely on an eccentric whim. I'm reminded of the old anecdote about the man invited to a masked ball who turned up, dressed as a court jester, his face caked in flour. The host family was peacefully chatting away at the fireside, where our hero joined them and where they spent a pleasant evening all together. And when he got up to go, his hosts told him in parting, 'not to forget the masked ball next Tuesday'.

Here, too, we're waiting for the pasta to cook. Here, too, we turn to the library to furnish the subject of our first conversation. A first discussion is often guided by one's nationality. The Italian likes to shine, the German to compare his own with others', while the Englishman, on his island, dissects the weather.

Among travellers and in social animals generally, there is that particular breed who fetishize new encounters, with some Don Juan-like instinct that leads them to enjoy only the first conversation. But all that has vanished in the world of fascism. The first conversation is a deadly serious game in which you have to try and figure out where your new acquaintance stands regarding the fascist state. In Hitler's *Reich*, even this game is too dangerous and a single word out of place can lead to untold suffering. The Italians have elevated this psychological game of poker to an art. They read the paper on the tram like born card players, poker-faced, like members of a secret society, and recognise each other from an inflection or a sigh. I play this game now, and the prince also plays, impeccably.

"I see you're interested in Napoleon."

"I have fourteen thousand volumes. We're related on my mother's side and it was my uncle who compiled the bibliography of sources related to his Italian campaign. He's the one who started the collection. Are you interested in Napoleon?"

"I must admit, not particularly."

"Most unusual. The majority of people are. Or rather, not so much in him, but in his career. They buy the first volume of his biography – they run with him, become Emperor, but no-one goes with him to Elba. They don't care for Ségur's excellent description of the Russian campaign. They may spend a minute of condolence on St Helena with Aubry and Las Casas, but that comes with age. There are far more kings without a throne over fifty, and they can empathise with Napoleon."

There's an entire cabinet full of various editions of Constant's memoirs.

"Did you know that this is the most successful book written about Napoleon? People like to get the butler's view on the great and the good. They only feel close to them when they see that the despot himself fits in the palm of their hand. Do you know whose are the most promising memoirs in Italy today?"

"To follow your thinking, Mussolini's butler."

"I think it's his lover's maid."

I sit down to my pasta relieved. The prince is looking forward to the Duce's death. This white pasta and parmesan is fantastic. It's the most democratic institution in fascism. There's no difference between Mr. Key's dinner and Don Agesilao's: they both eat pasta. This is why Italy lacks that deathly hatred that pits the soup-eater against the roast-meat eater. On the field of carbohydrates, there is full equality.

The prince pours a heavy, earthy Tuscan wine. The butler serves me first.

Nice antique Italian scores await on the piano. I'm not a skilled pianist – I couldn't play a Chopin étude. But on the harpsichord and the organ, I am in my element and Bach is my mother tongue. Even with my technical limitations, I can play his music, I know it so well.

"I see you have the works for organ, too."

"Yes, but sadly they're for three hands."

"Well, I can lend you two. The bass parts are not difficult".

Our three-handed playing goes well. We repeat a fugue three times, but by the end, it sounds ok.

"It would be nice if we had two pianos."

"Right you are, I'll buy another one."

Well said. You have to have a pretty respectable bank balance to be able to say that simple phrase so evenly, so calmly.

We play till eleven. How nice it would be if we could play a little more, and then the prince might say, 'It's getting late, why don't you stay the night?' But instead, he says:

"It's getting late and you must be wanting to get to bed."

It's true, this is indeed my dearest wish. But all I say is

"I have some time."

"I nearly forgot," says the prince, "you, of course, speak German. I have here a number of catalogues, De Gruyter, Fischer, Insel... would you do me the kindness of picking out any works relating to the Napoleonic period? I should be much obliged, indeed. By the day after tomorrow, say? Wonderful, I'll expect you the day after tomorrow at a quarter past eight."

The majordomo ushers me from the room, and hands me over in the staircase:

"Amadeo, would you please see the gentleman out?"

Amadeo accompanies me down the stairs, and since the concierge is already asleep, he opens a little door in the enormous gate. I know that it's customary to tip him, and I'm afraid Amadeo knows it too. Oh, well.

I leave.

Princes pour my wine, prisoners sole my shoes – that's life in the city of the Popes, but the churches still only open at five.

Not having the *Almanach de Gotha* to hand, I turn to my omniscient Baedeker for some information about my prince. Where was I again, last night? Anguillara. Ah, Palazzo Anguillara. Built in 1514 for an Orsini, gambled away in 1612 by another. Its façade is usually attributed to Rafael. It has a chapel, where a proven miracle once occurred. This being a Roman palazzo, it may well have been an obliging miracle.

I highlight the relevant books happily, the ones that may interest the prince. *Beiträge zur Kenntnis der Lepidopteren St Helenas.* That may be of interest, too. I'd like to know how much he'll pay for this work.

That evening, the Geographical Society is all aflutter in the Greco – Sommer and Gyurka Molnár are leaving us.

"I've found the country!" Sommer says. "We're going to sea. You don't need a visa for that! The Norwegian consul understood our predicament, and got us contracts as ship's doctors. In Norway, the shipping tonnage works out to one per capita – and they haven't got enough doctors. *Opholdstilladelse* means leave to remain. For now, we're headed to Narvik."

"Narvik! The ice floes, the middle of nowhere, peace!"

"Where is Narvik?"

"It's far," Sommer says rapturously, "very far."

"We're going on a whaling ship," Gyurka Molnár adds. "It'll be nice to vanish in the Arctic fog. Fog ahead, fog behind. In any case, there's too many eskimos here in Europe, and not enough seals."

"Think of the Titanic!"

But Sommer doesn't care. The only thing he's sorry about is that he has to leave now, when they've taken off the bars. I know a little bit of Danish, and so I offer: "I'll teach you the basics of the Scandinavian languages."

Sommer's delighted. "Good, plan, come to mine."

I hope his place also has a sofa. Key's injections are almost gone. We arrange the lessons.

I present myself at the palace, whose history I am now familiar with, the work all done. I greet Amadeo, the ancestor, the majordomo and the prince. I introduce myself to the new piano. It's a happy piano, it has a home. I hand over the list.

"Thank you," says the prince. "You're too kind, really. You have done me a great service."

But we don't waste our time in conversation. The works for organ are laid out, in two copies, on the pianos, which have been tuned, each to the other. We play like children with brand new toys. At midnight, my host gets tired.

"Where do you live?" he asks, "where can I reach you if we should play again?"

"At the moment I'm in between places, and I'm staying with a friend. Can I drop off my new address with the concierge when I'm settled?"

"I would be much obliged".

We take our leave.

In this situation, how am I supposed to tell him that I was expecting money? That the paper cost half a lira, which is two slices of pizza, and half the fee for an injection? This, I can explain neither in Italian, nor in English.

The majordomo hands me over to Amadeo. Amadeo opens the door. It's pouring with rain, that cold tropical rain that soaks you to your skin. It's a long way to the tram, and the house in the Via Lupe Tarpea has no roof. There's the all-night restaurant... and it's heated...

"Amadeo," I say discreetly, "dear Amadeo... you couldn't possibly lend me two lira? I don't know when I shall be able to give it back..."

Amadeo reaches into his pocket, looks briefly away, and with an incomparable, truly princely gesture, presses a five-lira coin into my hand.

"It's yours," he says.

Chapter XIII

Sometimes, the sun shines for a few days. Walking down the route of the Pincian Hill, even the homeless pity those who cannot enjoy the charm of the city, or rather, The City. Wasn't it Schiller who wrote an ode of jealousy to the beggars of Rome? On behalf of the addressees, I'd like to thank him from the bottom of my heart.

I actually more or less do have somewhere to live. Thanks to Miss Elsa's generosity, I can spend most of the day in the flat in the Via delle Vite, where I can sleep on Aldo's, or Pietro's bed. Pietro isn't home much, he's in talks with the Opera already, and his name – though in the smaller print – has appeared on one or two posters. Sometimes I sleep here from morning until noon, then at Key's in the afternoon, and then again here in the evening – and I am increasingly beginning to see it going on like this forever. It's only from midnight till six a.m. that I begin to doubt anew the feasibility of my current lifestyle.

Aldo dutifully keeps me updated on the progress of the battle for autarchy. The word "battle" is an essential element of this, and every other sort of activity. Sowing and reaping, harrowing and planting, are all part of the battle for wheat. Breastfeeding and changing nappies are done in the name of the battle for babies. Without struggle, nor assemblies under flags nor offensives nor victories, the presses of the Ministry run dry. There are even posters up on the walls declaring – "let us fight the flies!"

Actual work only takes place in the region between Teruel and Barcelona, where the fascist legions are busy clearing out the hills, and organising their positions with the Moroccan mercenaries.

The first victory has come in the bitter battle for self-sufficiency: they've managed to make a stable fibre from casein. Italy needs wool, and so instead of making cheese, they're weaving the milk. "Guns or butter?" asked Goebbels. "Cheese or trousers?" thunder Aldo and his colleagues. It turns out that it's possible to make shirts, and what's more black shirts, from fragrant *bel paese*. Photo: the first black shirt made from cheese.

Parmesan is proud to be contributing to this drive – its price jumps form one lira twenty to two lira. Ominous articles threaten the cheese speculators. And what's the good of cheese, anyway? It's a decadent habit, a bourgeois way of life. The fascist man lives on carbohydrates. He eats sugar. And that, with the help of sulphuric acid, you can even make from trees. And if there aren't enough trees (there's not much forest in Italy), then there's the good old home-grown lamb's wool. From wool and plastic, you can extrude a material that replaces the wood in furniture perfectly well. Photo: an original extruded Cremona violin.

Open yourselves to the penetrating mystery of autarchy, every paper enjoins. The language gains new expressions – till now, cheap goods were "for families". Now, there is something even flimsier – the *tipo autarchico*.

I have this struggle for autarchy to thank for an insight into my barber's mind, and for the lasting friendship that followed. For he, too, has had an idea:

"I like music," he told me, looking at the violin. "I like *Giovinezza* best. I'd like to hear it played on that violin." And then, looking me intently in the eyes, he says: "And I'd make the strings from the Duce's guts!"

I can't list all the various household products made from rabbit fur, potatoes, and hazelnut flour, because my time is devoted to Sommer.

We found a Norwegian Bible at the British Bible Society, and we're trying to derive those grammatical principles from the Apocalypse of St John, that may come in useful to a Hungarian dentist off on a whale-hunt. Sommer puts his dentist's drill into storage, because he secretly hopes to return. His minor possessions, he gives away – he gives me his needle, a box of novocaine, some distilled water, an old stethoscope, a few ampoules of calcium. Eventually, he asks me:

"Would you like my blood-pressure cuff? I'm not going to drag this big box halfway round the world."

A thought runs through my exhausted brain – what if Sommer is the man the gypsywoman was talking about? Maybe this big box will become my home…

I could go from house to house, taking people's blood pressure. I would charge a lira and a half. If I found ten clients, I could make a living. Or even five. I'd have a home if I could find just three. I could re-join the happy band of people who sleep in a bed!

"Yes, let me have it, I'll pay you in irregular verbs."

There's an old lady who sits at the Ponte Sant'Angelo selling pumpkin seeds. She has thirty little cones of seeds in front of her, and that's her shop. At night, she sleeps in a bed. On the Piazza Bernini, there's a man with a little table whose sole equipment consists of a screwdriver, a bag of cotton wool and a small bottle of petrol. He's been there for weeks, and he's still alive. He keeps himself alive by repairing and refilling lighters. And if he can do that, then it's certainly possible to make a living from a black box, a rubber cuff and a glass tube full of mercury. If Pietro, the Cobbler of Abruzzo, is soon to be the Barber of Seville, then perhaps I myself may be promoted to the Blood-Pressure-Taker of Rome.

I could even choose to see an obliging miracle in the black box – Mr Key's cure is over. We take emotional leave of each other, although he's used to his guests leaving him, sooner or later. He's stopped saying "see you soon."

I gaze at my treasure affectionately. There's not another soul who's spent such pleasant, indulgent hours in Sommer's dentist's chair as I have. I got to sleep there for two nights. This gave me the opportunity to prepare dreamily for my new profession.

Sommer has his papers, the Norwegian ship is coming to dock in Civitavecchia, but all of a sudden, he changes his mind. He won't go, he can't. He's been here for years, he likes the frascati and the pasta, the dome of St Peter's, his patients, his drill, and his little girl has been crying non-stop for days. He hates the Norwegians' irregular verbs. I have to give him back the cuff. Gyurka Molnár can go in his place, he's staying right here.

The same day, in Paris, a zealous Polish Jew shoots a German consular official dead. The Germans finally have their excuse for the pogrom they've planned to the last detail, like clockwork. They firebomb to the minute, destroy buildings in a regulation manner, murder from a list. There was a time when one man suffered for the sins of many. Now there aren't enough people to suffer for the sins of one man. Humanity learns a new lesson – that of mass-murder planned out with pencil and paper in an office somewhere. Till now, it was only a single man who murdered in cold blood; crowds always killed in the throes of some passion. We're making progress.

The next day, Sommer and Gyurka Molnár left for Civitavecchia. I, for my part, started on my own way, in search of some blood whose pressure I could take. I'm in luck. The second or third door opens. A fat, elderly man. You're measuring blood pressure? Excellent, I just wanted mine taken. It's been too high – come in. I take his pressure, it's a hundred and fifty. My patient – if I can call him that – is happy.

"It was a hundred and eighty last time. Wait a moment, would you go and see a friend of mine? He lives nearby, are you free? I'll call him now and tell him you're coming… How much did you say? Two lira? *Benissimo.*"

His friend also pays, and recommends me to someone else, too. My next patient is limping.

"What's your trouble?"

"Sciatica."

"Is that all? We'll soon fix that."

I have all of Sommer's inheritance with me – the needles, the syringes, and novocaine. I dilute the 4% solution to half that strength with water. I find the longest needle. Where does it hurt? There? Lie down. I go down until the nerve, and inject the solution. You can stand up now. Does it still hurt? No? Good.

The whole thing went so quickly that the patient can hardly believe it. Are you sure it isn't some kind of a swindle? Won't the pain come back? I don't think so, I tell him, but if it does I can come back and we'll do the procedure again.

"How much do I owe you?"

I know that this is a watershed moment – I have to say a number without hesitation, calmly. I screw up my courage and say deliberately: "Thirty lira."

My patient reaches into his pocket. 'My god,' I think to myself, 'I could just as well have said fifty! Never mind. Tonight, I'm sleeping in a bed.' I go on my way elated, like someone who's just been lucky at cards. By the end of the afternoon, I have more than forty lira in my pocket. That'll be enough for today. I go see the barber, with whom I'm so friendly by now that I already owe him three lira. We talk.

"You don't happen to know of a room somewhere nearby? Or even just a bed?"

But Figaro knows everything.

"But of course. Just a stone's throw from here, right next door to me. Do you know the Via della Rapa? Carrot street? Turn there, then take a right, straight on, and right again. Number fifteen, first floor. For thirty lira, they'll give you a bed. She's a good woman, I know her."

Straightaway, I'm off, like some latter-day Archimedes – give me a bed in which to sleep, and I'll move the world! The streets I've been directed to go back several centuries into

Rome's past. First floor. The bell is a chain-pull affair. There's a bed to let here. Here, right here. In the hallway, or in the little nook off the hallway, separated by a little curtain.

This time, I look not at the landlady, but at the splendour of the bed. A real bed, with four iron legs, a mattress, and a blanket. I look at it like Sommer at the Norwegian steamer.

"Do you have any luggage?"

"I'll bring it over later."

"Do you have a police registration card?"

"Yes, of course…"

"Occupation?"

I say proudly and firmly:

"Blood Pressure Specialist."

I can see that it has the right effect. Now it's my turn to ask some questions:

"Sheets?"

"There aren't any, but you can bring your own."

"Bathroom?"

"There isn't one, but you can come to an arrangement with the family across the hall."

If I draw the curtain and lie on the bed, I can stay during the day. Aside from me, there's only one other tenant – Mario, a government functionary whose office is opposite the church of *Sant Andrea della Valle*. The thirty lira is payable in advance.

I try to imitate Amadeo's dignified movement. "There you are. I'll be back this evening with my things. Until then, I'm leaving the blood pressure machine here. Take good care of it, it's irreplaceable and priceless!"

I go back to the Via delle Vite and let them know I've managed to find a suitable place to stay. Miss Elsa and Francesca seem genuinely happy for me. And Pietro is moving out too. In the space of a week, his name has grown a centimetre on the posters – he's got his contract. He's moving closer to the Opera. Aldo asks me to give him two German lessons a week – his career in the Ministry depends on it. In ten years, you won't be able to hold a senior position without knowing German. As payment, he offers me a pair of his old trousers; its knees are perfectly intact. I accept the deal with pleasure, keenly aware how important it is in the liberal professions that one's right knee should not show through one's trousers.

My bed greets me warmly, like the prodigal son. I wake up sometime after midnight, and imagine what it would be like to be going round and round Rome now on the *circolare*, straining to hear what time the clocks have just rung, in the cold night rain... and I go back to sleep happily, like a child on its mother's bosom. I wake again at eight, in bed. I'm back.

Chapter XIV

Taking people's blood pressure is a fine profession. I can strongly recommend it to homeless doctors. If I should once again end up somewhere with only my little suitcase for company – life being basically a cyclical process – I would get straight to it. Want to know your blood pressure? *Óhajtja, hogy megmérjem a vérnyomását? El presión del sangre?* To be on the safe side, I've found out that a blood pressure cuff is called a *'katsu-atsu'* in Japanese. But I do have my reservations about doing it in a fascist country. It's a dangerous profession. Aldo tells me so when he spots the little black notebook in my pocket – a name on every page, addresses, numbers. Locatelli, RR 130/90, Ricci 150/95, Lucchi 134/100.

"If the police catch you, you're finished!"

"I've nothing to fear. I'll just tell them what it's all about."

"You're wrong. They'll just put you in jail. Even before you got a chance to say a word, they'd interrogate those twenty or thirty people. 'Do you know the owner of this book? No? Then how come your name's in it? What does 130/90 mean?' They don't know. They deny all knowledge. They confront them with the others.' They say they don't know each other, but then there they all are on the same list! You're already in deep trouble before you've had a chance to open your mouth."

I begin to understand. What was it that Bakó said? The paranoiac sees a giant conspiracy. The police are looking for conspirators. They finally catch someone with a little black book. They have their list, the numbers. A bunch of people flatly denying everything. There might even be one or two among them with a criminal record. The police officer who gets to the bottom of it will be promoted a general! And I should explain to him that 130 is the systolic, and 90 the diastolic pressure...

I take more care, especially where I have to skirt the route of the secret policemen. Sommer's equipment is not the most modern, a cumbersome, leather-cased thing with an aneroid – a heavy, clumsy, black box, with a mercury manometer and a lengthy scale. It does the patient good to watch me erect the intricate machine in front of them, then put the mercury back down to zero, but I'm afraid the dutiful Calabrian detectives would take it for some kind of bomb. If one of them collared me he probably wouldn't even let me open it up to show him – he'd probably think I was trying to send us both sky high, take me straight to the police station, and hand my doomsday machine over to the sappers to be rendered harmless.

A nagging sense of guilt arises. What if I really am walking around with a bomb? What if I am the conspirator-in-chief? I look at people's faces – have they recognised me? I think about what I would say at the police station and at the Extraordinary Tribunal. A single judge has handed down twenty thousand years. I wonder how many people that was to. What will Mr. Key say when he sees me? Should I hide the contraption under my coat, or should I carry it with my head innocently high and a smile of my face, as if it were nothing but a toy? Or should I write "barometer" on it?

I have to be careful, there's a hunt going on, and the quarry is human. Among the natives of Borneo, a young man cannot get married until he brings his betrothed a human head. It's quite a useful little custom, and far the simplest form of birth control on an island which can only support so many people, making it also a just institution. It's not a question of passion or cruelty, but of necessity.

But the white man has his own way of hunting: he hunts with laws, to catch a killer on the run, for example. But beyond that, the modern head-hunter crawls along on rooftops to shoot people, glides around in cars, or at least watches the hunt on the silver screen, reads about it in books. Trapping a man in the urban jungle, taking him in, locking him in a cage, that is the ruling passion and the daily bread of this ilk. The Calabrians with their invisible presence are born hunters, they have their nose and their trusty instincts. In the good old days, they would rob travellers. Their hunting grounds were lonely country roads, but fascism put an end to all that and made the poachers into gamekeepers. They're still hunting on the roads, only now it's legal and comes with pension rights.

I can feel the heat of the hunt – and I see the prey fleeing, Sommer and Rosenwurz, or staying and hoping, trusting themselves to the shelter of the terrain. A picture of Göring, the Master of the Hunt, hangs outside the offices of the *Giornale d'Italia.* They're shooting hares as they run, and the borders are all patrolled. Even the Swiss are shooting at people approaching their border without a pass. In the Czech highlands, they're hunting Socialists. My imagination reaches over the limits of probability – I dream that somewhere near Weimar, where Goethe so liked to stroll, deep in the beech forests, the natives are shrinking heads until they become tiny, simian fetishes, and drying someone's tattooed skin on a wooden frame…

Best be careful with the blood pressure taking!

But it's not enough merely to avoid the secret policemen, there are also the concierges to watch out for! They are the best and most reliable pillars of the state. Ministers here are puppets who come and go, but the concierges are the guards who are always on duty. They have their letters patent, and to get them they should preferably have been, or be any (or all) of the following: party members, front-line soldiers, fathers of large families, war-cripples and former paramilitary sergeant-majors. Not to mention that they have to be literate. There are, however, exceptions made to that last criterion; for example, the concierge in the house in the Via della Rapa thankfully cannot read or write. In his defence, he's seventy and has been in his post for fifty years now.

The concierge stands in the gate, on the lookout. They regularly confer with the police. Who comes and goes, where? Who has lots of visitors? Who gets letters, where from? Ever seen any anti-fascist graffiti in the staircase? If there ever is any, it's not enough for the concierge to get rid of it, he also has to inform the police. Who could have written it? When? Did any strangers come to the house?

The Duce has a monopoly on the writing on the wall. It is a legal requirement that the walls of every peasant house near a public building, railway or major road should be painted with one of the Duce's more important maxims. "A nation's consumption of soap is a measure of its civilisation," or "Fascism begins at home," or "I predict that in a hundred years, the whole world will be fascist," I cannot die before my task is done," and "I have a thousand years work ahead of me". I can easily understand why the concierge might be scared of someone taking a black box inside his building – there might be chalk in it!

I quickly learn what a conciergerocracy is like. The residents aren't afraid of the Duce, they're afraid of the concierge. The concierge is the eyes of the state. He's the one who goes through your dustbin to find out what you've been eating. He's the one who takes your suspicious letter to the police. He is the representative of the totalitarian state. There are plenty of people who are happy to read about the decisive victory over the Loyalists in Spain over their eggs and coffee, there are those who keep happy memories of Vittorio Emmanuele and Hitler inspecting the fleet at Naples, but if the Duce's spies could look into their hearts, they would realise that the rot has begun – even they already detest their concierges. Heed the warning signs! People are smiling at them, and bribing them. All is not well.

I try all sorts of ruses. I approach the concierge straight off: "Would you like me to take your blood pressure?"

The concierge is often bored, and sometimes has it done. I can go up. Or, I'll ask "Is this number 111? Someone called me to take their blood pressure. I can't remember the name. You wouldn't happen to know who it was, would you?" The concierge knows all: "Yes, it was the woman in number fourteen, she's always complaining of her heart on the stairs."

I'm happy if I get the four or five patients a day I need to support myself. Some people ask me to come monthly. If

I could get a hundred steady cases... For the moment, if I make my ten lira, I shut up shop for the day. Eight lira I spend on food and culture, and the other two I set aside for my rent and for unforeseen expenses. Slowly, I built up my strength and start to notice the world again. When I wasn't sleeping, I dozed through events. There are talks between Germany and France, "in the spirit of Munich", one newspaper reports. That's a spirit they like better East of the Rhine.

I start to sort out my personal affairs, too. I give the prince my new address. I could add that I myself am now living in a noble *palazzo* – this was once the old, elegant face of Rome, and Rossini himself lived nearby in the *Via della Vacche* – the street of cows. Here sits also the house where Cardinal Pacelli was born. The poor have taken over the dark buildings, their castle walls and red-brick floors. There are workshops where coach-houses used to be, but even so the way to my tiny quarters is through an immense gate and vaulted corridors.

Ever since I tipped him handsomely, Amadeo has been especially kind to me – would I like to play the piano by myself? Yes of course!

"Does the prince live alone?"

"The princess hasn't left their estate near Padova in years. The two boys are at university in Padova, too. The little girl, Diana, is at the Sacré Coeur. So yes, the prince lives alone."

I go see the Bakós too – the "Geographical Society" hasn't met since Sommer and Molnár left. I bring them some flowers, my conscience is not altogether clear, and I am a little ashamed before these people who knew me when I was homeless – as if I'd cut my fish with the wrong knife. There's some Hungarians visiting – two football coaches. I find out that there are almost a hundred of them. There's Kettő Kertész, Ferencváros's lanky, immortal defender, and Schlosser, the legendary striker...

"Hungarian coaches are the best," one of them tells me, "but there's one thing even we can't explain to the Italians – that the game is played by eleven men with one ball. These Italians think there should be eleven balls!"

Bakó asks me how I make my living. I tell him, and he congratulates me.

"That's what the people need! You see, I know that psychiatry is just a game. Do you know what I'd do if I had the money? I'd open a calcium bar, somewhere near the Piazza Colonna. You could walk in off the street and for ten lira, you'd get a calcium shot, a vitamin pill, your blood pressure taken, and your lung capacity measured, and maybe even a shave. In a year, we'd be rich! Step right in, to the fountain of health! Act today and get a free treatment to dissolve your uric acid!"

"What treatment is that?"

"A glass of water. Don't you know that uric acid dissolves in water?"

Bakó's wife is ashamed – it's the scientist in her husband that she loves.

"You don't understand how serious I am about this." Then he turns to me: "You're going about it the wrong way. You should go and sit in a pharmacy. When someone gets sick here, they turn first to the woman next door, then to Saint Anthony, and then the pharmacy. The doctor doesn't even come into it. You should go sit in a pharmacy and wait for the patients to come to you."

The policemen and the concierges – I'd be safe from all of them in a pharmacy!

The narrow little alley that leads to the magnificent Piazza Navona starts on the corner of the Via della Rapa. Just before the square there's an ancient pharmacy. The pharmacist mixes his laxatives among blue painted ceramic pots and archaic mortars, making the street famous among the locals as the *Via della Purgo*. I've chatted with the pharmacist before, and I think I could mention the idea to him.

I tell him my plan:

"How would it be if I came and sat in your shop one or two hours a day and took people's blood pressure? The place doesn't seem too busy anyway."

He's fine with it, but wants me to talk it over with the pharmacy's doctor first. The aged doctor fits marvellously among the porcelain pots. He's a true Roman, and as such, is very kind to foreigners. Rome has been a cosmopolitan city for two thousand years, the capital of an empire, the home of a religion, how could Rome not understand every mother's son?

"How long have you been in Italy? Do you like Rome?"

"Oh yes, yes."

"How's your Italian?"

I lay out my plan to him, too, and how it won't disturb him in his little camphorous lair. In fact, if a patient's blood pressure is too low or too high, I can bring them straight to him. It would be best if I came in the morning, and then again at half past five, when his shift starts.

"Very well. *Benone.*"

So I go and sit in the pharmacy, behind a little table, and we make a sign: "Have your blood pressure checked! 2 lira." It turns out that the pharmacy is busier than I thought – it's never empty. Only the old jars stay empty, the pharmacist reaching under the counter to draw out his cornucopia of laxatives. These are cooked up by an impressively ugly Neapolitan woman over in the laboratory on the left. On the right is the doctor's office, while in the back are the darkened recesses of the stockroom.

The pharmacist has spent the day telling his customers that the pharmacy was now offering a blood-pressure-taking service. As a result, I sometimes have as many as three people waiting for my services by the afternoon.

I take their blood pressure, and note them neatly down on the pharmacy's official paper – 2nd December 1938, Name, Age. 142/102.

"There you are."

"How is it?"

"A hundred and forty two… how old are you? Thirty-eight? It's a little high. A hundred and thirty-eight would be better. You'd best speak to the doctor…"

"Is it dangerous?"

"Not at all, but it's still best if we have a little chat."

We go into the doctor's little room. We are all very serious, as if it were a trial. The judge sits in the armchair. I lead the accused in and sit him down on a small round stool. The armchair, by comparison, projects majesty. I ask for silence, and then I open for the prosecution.

"Your honour! The accused, despite being only thirty-eight years old, has produced a pressure in his right brachial artery that has displaced a hundred and forty-two millimetres of mercury! He has therefore transgressed the law that says that the pressure should not exceed the person's age plus a hundred."

The impartial judge listens without so much as a flutter of emotion. He won't judge before the accused has had a chance to speak for himself.

"Do you smoke?"

"Yes."

"Drink?"

"Sometimes."

The judge deliberates. What will his judgement be? He can't say yet. He wants one more proof, he takes out his old stethoscope and presses it to the patient's chest across the table. He listens for a tense, exciting minute, and then passes sentence:

"You're to take three tablets of depressin a day."

The patient asks, "Before, or after meals?"

"Twenty minutes after eating!"

And then, to soften the blow of the sentence with some fatherly advice, he adds, "And watch out for those cigarettes."

Depressin is a harmless medicine. It contains potassium iodide, garlic extract, mistletoe, and a tenth of a milligram of nitro-glycerine. It can be found on the right-hand side of the counter.

The procedure with low blood pressure is exactly the same, but the sentence is different. The accused gets coramine, twice twenty drops. This is on the left-hand side of the counter.

By the third day, we have learned our roles to perfection. The whole thing goes like clockwork. Depressin and coramine; right and left. Coramine and Depressin. We know the outcome before the trial even starts. This is my living, and the doctor and pharmacist make a little money from it too. The patients are satisfied.

And it is in this that our little process differs from the very similar ones enacted non-stop in the red-brick building next to the river that has been assigned to the Extraordinary Tribunal, among somewhat less happy circumstances.

Chapter XV

"*L'odeur du monde est changée*" – *there is a new world odour* – Duhamel says in one of his books, when discussing the turning point of a life. Nothing reflects a changed world better than the changing flavour of the air. I have stepped into a new world in Rome, in this city which is an old and silent witness to history. In this world, the area around the Piazza Navona is the living past, not the ancient past, like the Forum. The pharmacy, with its herbaceous odour, is the inner bastion of these defences, and its doctor's station (smelling of camphor) and smoky, disorderly laboratory are secret hiding places. This is where I hide from the hunt outside.

This is where I get to know the beneficent roots and barks, which until now have been nothing but names and concepts in my mind. I feel I ought to bow down before the dried leaves of the fox-glove, and it is with similar respect that I approach the light-brown, desiccated bits of cinchona bark – that bitter enemy of deadly fevers, whose powder the Jesuits once considered worth its weight in gold. Radix rhei and cortex condurango, sarsaparilla and valerian have all become my friends. I almost expect to find the powdered horn of a unicorn, a dried-out mummy, a jar of leeches.

"There's a pharmacist in Trastevere who still keeps leeches, and he does quite well out of it," the old doctor tells me. "Unfortunately, we have to move with the times."

"You don't know Rome at all," he then adds spitefully.

"I was here ten years ago," I say in my defence.

This placates the old man somewhat, as if I'd told him that a patient's blood pressure isn't really a hundred and eighty after all, but only a hundred and seventy-five.

"In '28," he says, "the *Borgo* was still standing. That beautiful little square was still there, half-way between St Peter's and the *Castel Sant'Angelo,* where Raphael had his house. The old fountain in the middle sits there now like an orphaned child.

Did you see it? Do you remember what it was like when you came out of the narrow little streets into St Peter's? You could see the roofs and the hanging gardens on the balconies from the turret of the *Castel Sant'Angelo*, the same one they shoot Cavaradossi on in Tosca."

"Yes, I remember," I lie, the sparse squares that replaced the old Borgo having as thoroughly supplanted the memory in my mind as the dumpy woman has the frail young girl with the sunken eyes.

"What do you remember?" the doctor says dismissively. "The staircases, the vaulted entranceways, the old cauldrons in the ancient kitchens. That's where I started practicing. I was an assistant in the *Ospedale dello Spirito Santo*, in the Borgo. Do you know it?"

"I've passed it."

"Ah, but you haven't been inside! You should see the library! But who goes there any more? It was Lancisi's collection. He died in the 1720s, in 1721 I think, and the books haven't moved an inch since then. There they sit and wait for the disciples of Galen and Hippocrates. Worm-eaten books, cracked manuscripts, but what a wealth of knowledge! Don't think for a moment that the doctors of old were fools! We still have plenty to learn from them. Go see the *Spirito Santo*! And have you seen the old quarter between the Piazza Venezia and the Colosseum? The old *Accademia San Luca*? Do you know, I've never walked on the *Via del Imperio*, and I never will! I'd burst out crying. It's appalling, what the Italians are doing to Rome."

I look at him in slight puzzlement – he didn't say "the fascists," he said "the Italians."

"When they broke in at the Porta Pia in 1871, and believe me it was no glorious feat blowing a hole in the wall, my father hid in the cellar and didn't come out for three months. Have you seen prince Lancelotti's palace on the corner there? He locked the great gate and for fifty years came and went by the back door, waiting for the Italians to leave. The red-hats went around in carriages, didn't even touch the cobbles of the city. We didn't ask Garibaldi, we didn't need the Savoys. Under the Popes we paid no tax and a lamb cost four *baiocci*!" He shows me the size of a brass four-baiocco coin.

"That's when all the trouble started. They wanted a capital. They could have built it outside the walls, there was plenty of room. But they wanted to come here. They moved half of Milan here, the apartment buildings on the Piazza Barberini! They wanted to destroy what was old. The world would be in awe of what Rome used to be like! Oh, how the Capitol used to look, till they put that marble cage over it! And now they treat the very core of the city as an enemy, because it's holding up the traffic. They're going to bulldoze the little that's left. They're talking about an aerial war, but let them come, the bombers, because the city has already been destroyed. The old boroughs are already gone, and one of these days they'll clean up our little district too. I hope by then to be under the tall trees."

But for me, who never saw the ancient glories, even what's left is a lot. I like the castle-like walls of my building, and I'm grateful for my street that's too narrow to allow cars to pass on its higgledy-piggledy cobbles. That's where I have my meals, in the rosticceria there, the cheese and tomato Neapolitan pizzas cooked over charcoal. And this is where my barber is, too. After all, it was he who introduced me to this enchanted part of town. We've gotten to be quite friendly since he told me about his musical ambitions. I know the story of his life. He used to live in Syracuse and had been a member of the Socialist party since his apprentice days. He already had his own shop when the fascists came. One day, they called him in to the party headquarters.

"Join today," they told him, "and you'll go far."

"I won't join."

"We'll smash your shop to smithereens."

"I'll bet you won't."

"You'll see tomorrow."

He went home, took out his hatchet, and that very evening smashed the chairs and mirrors up so thoroughly that the fascists themselves couldn't have done a better job. Then he came here. He worked three years as an apprentice again. His shop now is a pale imitation of the old one, but he's his own master again. They leave him alone here. He shaves well, and I am absolutely convinced that he knows more about interna-

113

tional diplomacy than Count Ciano, the foreign minister. It's true that that hardly makes him unique among the barbers.

"Here in town you're hardly aware of fascism, but in the countryside they keep tabs on everyone."

I often watch him at work. If whoever's chin he's scraping happens to be a like-minded individual, he talks. If a stranger comes in, and that stranger conforms to Attilio's masterful description, he keeps silent as the tomb.

"Do you know who's safest here?" he asks me once, confidentially. "The deaf-mutes. They have their club over by the *Chiesa Nuova*. They can't pin them down. They can really speak their minds."

He pushes his chin forward, and draws the razor horizontally across his throat. "I don't need words, either!"

Bakó may be right, and these dictatorships of black will one day drown under their own weight. But the League of Nations should preserve a little "specimen territory," to educate the true believers for six months or a year, to show them what it's really like, living under the rule of a Leader.

Here, in this part of the city, there are moments when I, too, forget – when I draw the curtain in front of my bed. I heard that sometimes they put a rope cordon between the beams on the top of skyscrapers under construction so that the workers will feel safer. So is my curtain a rope cordon at the edge of the abyss.

I have yet to see my landlady, however. I spoke to Mario, the man who rents the room, one Sunday morning. He's a simple boy, from the South; he supports his elderly parents, his sister, and her two children too. His brother-in-law died in Abyssinia – on one occasion, six hundred Italians were killed in a single day. They got drawn into an ambush. The newspaper, of course, stayed silent about the whole thing. But his sister applied to the Ministry of African Affairs, and that's how Mario got this job, not at the ministry itself but in the banana monopoly they controlled. He sends every penny home, and works a second job from two in the afternoon until ten at night to make a little money for himself.

In one respect, I have already become truly Roman – I don't leave my neighbourhood, named after the bridge, unless I absolutely have to. All the more so because the merry-go-round tram is good for sleeping on, but useless as a means of public transport. It doesn't even dare enter the city, just goes round and round outside the walls. The bus is expensive, crowded and uncomfortable. A real Roman may live near the station, but he never travels.

I sometimes wander out of my neighbourhood to take someone's blood pressure, but I only go to the people I know already. I have quietly renounced my patients who live farther out. My longest walks are when I go to give Aldo his German lesson or when homesickness takes me to the Greco, where I am now happy to buy the immortal bard a pastry.

"Thank you, Great Blood Pressure Taker!"

Aldo really is making a great effort to learn. He has a good head for it and limitless ambition. He knows that a "cultural compact" will be made between Italy and Germany and his career depends on *"der-die-das."* *Der* in this case being *der Führer.* He's determined to make it to undersecretary at the very least.

"Why do you think I did my PhD in political science? Three years of university! And why do you think my father took part in the March on Rome? So I could spend my whole life in some poky office?"

"Your father marched on Rome with Mussolini?"

"No, he didn't march, but he did send a telegram expressing his sympathies. And that's more or less the same thing. And besides, Mussolini didn't march either, but waited to see if it would work and then came up the next day by sleeper. Repeat it once again for me, *'Die Erben des Knaben haben drei Ziegen'* [The boy's heir has three goats]... by this time next year, I have to be able to follow the radio."

We crack on with the formation of verbs. "It's not good to mess around with the Germans."

But it is fun to mess with the French. The anti-French newspaper campaign is mostly the preserve of the funnies. Under the headline *'Ça, c'est Paris'* [This is Paris], they run endless cartoons showing how French women cheat on their husbands, who are not at all displeased, how they make love from morning till night, but have no children, bringing forth nothing but Africans. Decadent, drunk French officers say ridiculous things about the 'young nations'. Aldo has no comment.

"That's not our department."

Whoever's department it is, it's certainly thorough in its work. They focus on what is for them bad, or at least, what can be easily ridiculed in the French with a consistency so intense, it's as if the spotlight in the theatre only lit one person, leaving the rest of the stage in total darkness. It's hard to tell what the point of all this is just now, when in theory, the Franco-German pact of friendship is to be signed any day. Do Italians not like this new development? Or does Germany get better terms if the French are worried about the eight million bayonets in their lower regions? Is it all part of a well-developed campaign that the Italians are throwing mud at the French, and the Germans at the English? Or is it more accurate to see a difference in opinion here between the two countries?

The fact remains that in the spotlight where so recently the image of the mosque shone radiant, Marianne now sits, her figure rudely distorted. 'There is not a war lost with whose glorious deeds one could not fill a novel.' And there is not a nation on earth whose history does not involve its own Panama, Bluebeard and Battle of Sedan. Throwing mud is of course merely one part of war – idealism, noble and touching calls to action are clearly the province of yet another department. In the arc of the spotlight, a military cemetery appears. In the last War, an Italian division fought bravely outside Bligny, and a lot of people died. They have, until now, been buried in French soil, waiting for the last trump. Now, instead, they have the loudspeakers of the Ministry blaring above their heads. In the space of a week, the entire nation learns the name of this little French village. "Bring our poor dead home!" They start collecting money in steel helmets, the flood of telegrams begins. "In support of the families of the fallen of Bligny, the association of recipients of the Gold Medal of Military Valour" reads the telegram of the Association to the Ministry of Defence. The Duce sends a telegram to the Italian fascio in Paris. The papers report the German media's reaction to the incident. The only people keeping stubbornly silent about the whole thing are the quiet bones in Bligny.

I have to go see Cabillaud. I just want to hear a French voice in response to all this! After all, we live a stone's throw from each other, the French Church being just the other side of the Piazza Navona. I don't even have to leave my beloved neighbourhood. Every time I leave the house with my black box, I pass by it, even though there is a secret policeman between the Senate and the Church of St Louis. He knows me already, so I'm not afraid. Doctors and secret policemen don't like to practise on people they know.

Cabillaud is a little surprised by my visit. Maybe he thinks I've come for confession, or I want to talk to him about some spiritual breach. He sits in front of three hundred volumes of the Church Fathers in Greek and Latin like a cigar-smoking apostle.

"It's been a long time."

"I don't go much to the Greco any more. I work in a pharmacy here in the neighbourhood. I was passing this way, I thought I'd come and ask if I could come and play the organ sometimes... I could use a little Bach..."

"It's not up to me, my son. I am the spiritual leader and father confessor of the Sacré Coeur, and we have no organ up there. The nuns sing accompanied by a harmonium. But I will certainly mention it to the *regnus chori* if I see him. I know how much this means to you."

"What do you think, *reverendissime,* will there be war?"

He looks into the distance, whether into the future or into the past, I'm not sure.

"People never learn. The problem is that you can sum up the great truths, the really important things, in a few words but," he looks at the patristic literature around him, "you can never communicate it, even in the very greatest of books. Will there be war? Ask Nostradamus, our great seer! He has wonderful prophecies!"

"What did he say about today?"

"That, we'll find out tomorrow. He mixed his learned lines together so thoroughly that navigating them is a science in itself. Try it, my young friend! What is that black box you have?"

117

"I was on my way to a patient to take their blood pressure. Would you like me to take your blood pressure, Monsignore?"

I don't at all think he wants his blood pressure taken, and am somewhat surprised when he says, "*Pourquoi pas?*" [Why not?]

Maybe he's bored, among his books. Maybe he's also one of those who are fascinated by everything to do with their own bodies.

I inflate the cuff, I feel the artery. Yikes! The scale on the old box hardly goes up this high. His blood pressure is 255.

"Well?"

"It's high, Monsignore, very high."

"What does that mean?"

"You should be careful, Monsignore, with the cigars." I daren't tell him to take depressin.

"*Oh la la*! A few cigars! One of the attaches at the Embassy brings them for me from Havana. I don't even smoke that many, no more than four or five."

"That's not so much, in a year."

"*Mais non*! A day."

"Then it is a lot. The heart is an adding machine. It'll add up the daily dose and in a few years, it'll hand you the bill. Fifteen hundred a year is a lot!"

"What should I do?"

"Let's try to cut down to four or five a year."

"You doctors are always saying that giving things up is the best medicine, too. I'd like to know what you told people to give up before Columbus discovered the Americas!"

"We didn't have blood pressure monitors back then!"

"You know what? I'll give up having my blood pressure taken. But all that aside, come by from time to time, when the opportunity allows. And as I say, I'll talk to the organist."

What a serious man I had thought Monsignore Cabillaud! Now it turns out he believes in prophecies, in Nostradamus! But he knows people at the French Embassy, and it'll be useful to stay on good terms with him. And it feels good to come here, onto French territory where those awful newspapers aren't even allowed. Here, the Italian newspapers are represented by the Papal *Osservatore* and that is free of all influence from Aldo – or from any other of the Ministry's departments, for that matter.

December is cold even in Rome, especially since the people who built this town, in their sense of innate optimism, neglected to install fireplaces. Double-glazing is entirely unknown here. The brick floor of my room is cold as ice, and my curtain flutters in the draught. I suddenly realise that a bed is not the be all and end all – our honeymoon has come to an end. I no longer throw myself under the covers at eight, no longer grip the house-key feverishly in my pocket, like a rare treasure. Sometimes, I even go to the cinema where I listen to the projector's incomprehensible Italian babbling for hours on end... sometimes the Greco draws me back, though Sommer, Rosenwurz and Molnár are long gone, much to the detriment of the "Geographical Society."

Péter Pogány is an infrequent visitor, too, since he's working on his thesis, but we did bump into each other once.

"Where are you working?"

"In a pharmacy. And you?"

"In the Biblioteca Nazionale. Why don't you come up one afternoon, if you have the time?"

"Yes, why not? I could come by tomorrow. It'll be nice to read something again!"

The Swedish painter puts in an appearance, too. I'm curious about his work, I owe him a visit and I'd like to brush up my Swedish, too. I say goodbye to Pogány and say hello to Andersen.

"You promised to show me your paintings."

"I could show you them tonight. Come over to my studio."

Via Margutta was born a quiet place. It hid at the base of the Pincian hill, and let its parallel neighbour, the *Via Paviano*, with which it is united at beginning and end by two little squares, take most of the traffic. If a few of the workshops facing the street had not been turned into garages, it would have kept its place as an island of peace. It has none of the cafes or bars of Montmartre, it's a respectable street. Sculptors, framers, a photographer – these are the citizens of the Republic of the *Via Margutta*. The Republic is governed by its artists – whose honorific is *professore*. Their studios are at the top of the houses, and their big windows look onto the green of the Villa Borghese as if they were hothouses which sheltered the rarest blooms.

'Endre Mák,' it says on Andersen's studio door.

"I'll be off soon, the owner's coming back," he explains. "Let me go first, it's a little hard to find the way. Just stay there."

He puts on the light, and I can see what he means – the floor is covered with dozens, no hundreds, of empty wine bottles, narrow paths among them leading to the stove, the desk, and the window.

"So you're leaving soon?"

"Yes, I'll be here for Christmas, but then I'm going home. I don't want to get into any trouble!"

"You mean war?"

"There's definitely something coming. You see, the Germans are always planning something for the spring. Do you know what happened on my way here? A German gentleman joined my compartment at Copenhagen. It was just the two of us, we got talking. He was a very cultured man, interested in art, knew all the museums in Copenhagen. He was happy when he found out I was Swedish, said the Danes are still stuck on the battle of Dybbøl, they don't understand the new Germany. Then he suddenly got up and pointed to one of the stations.

'Look, that's my station!'

'What?'

'I'm an expert on railways, I'm one of the directors of the Berlin traffic bureau. If we should ever be forced to take over the Danish transport system, for example if we need to shut down the European system of transport from one day to the next, then this is where I'll be based. My Danish is already quite good. Two hundred and eighty-four trains go through here every day, of which seventy-eight per cent are goods trains.'

Those were the figures he mentioned. He knew all the signals and the points. I'm going home in January, whatever happens."

I looked around for his pictures, but I couldn't see them at all. There was, however, a strangely brown shrivelled skull on the mantelpiece.

"A sculpture?" I asked.

"No, a friar!"

"You mean it's a real skull?"

"Yes. Up on the *Via Veneto* the Capucins have their ossuary in the basement of a church. It's a hell of a place. Desiccated friars in open caskets just lying around, whole piles of spines, mountains of bones. That's where I pinched it from. I'm taking it home as a souvenir."

"But if they catch you...A hundred years ago, they were still stoning people who didn't kneel before the papal procession!"

"There's an old, bearded type at the door. I showed him a silver five-lira. He was so moved, he bowed so low he couldn't see what I had in my hand."

"Five lira is a lot of money," I admit (it's four days of pizza!).

"It wasn't real."

"You mean it was fake?"

"You'd better be careful with five lira coins! If you get one, you should throw it on the ground and see if it rings true. I got taken in at the start, too. I changed a hundred lira – they gave me all fives, and five of them turned out to be fake. Of course, I tried to pass them off, but everyone knew better than me. There was nothing for it, I didn't want to just throw it away, so once when I was in St Peter's, at the bit where they kiss the Saint's feet, I threw them in the collection box."

"I'm sure the priests were able to spend them."

"No doubt. Especially since I threw the real ones in by mistake. Tell me, have you ever noticed which bit of the sculptures in that church is most heavily worn, after St Peter's feet?"

"No."

"The backsides of the angels guarding Canova's tomb. That's the faithful for you."

Andersen tells me his stories, but I'm more curious about his pictures.

"And your paintings?"

"Oh, I've been very busy – a still life of Olevano, Piazza San Marco, the Lateran Basilica with the late autumn dry leaves all around; a monkeypuzzle tree on the Gianicolo with clinging purple creepers in its pink branches..."

"But where are all these pictures?"

"In my head. But I can describe them down to the last detail for you. Putting them onto canvas is no work at all. It's childsplay. It's seeing them that's the difficult part, choosing the right colours, the tone, the composition. Nature plays, the artist creates. Reality belongs to the machine. Art belongs to the living soul. I never touch purely mechanical things."

He gets up and, with an uncanny self-assurance, fishes out the one bottle which still has some wine in it. He pours and drinks. I drink too, hoping it'll clear things up for me.

"The art is in knowing how to see. The greatest art, believe me, is dreaming. If you can put your dreams, thick with symbolism, into words, then you're a poet. If you can paint them in oils, you're a painter. Being an artist means dreaming right, clearly, accessibly, colourfully. So beautifully that you can lull your fellow men to sleep. You know what Musset says about the goal of a poem: *éterniser un rêve - to fix a dream*. It's the same with painting. It's hard to dream, my dear sir. Daubing is a doddle."

"Fill me up, my dear Andersen, I think I'm beginning to understand..."

Chapter XVI

The next day, the prince's concierge brings me news: the prince has invited me for Saturday at a quarter past eight. 'I picked up a few interesting scores on a recent trip to Milan,' Don Agesilao writes.

How nicely everything is shaping up. When I'm in the pharmacy, inflating the pressure cuff, I can well imagine myself growing old doing it. One fine day, it may even be me in the armchair, handing down the sentence of 'depressin' or 'coramine.' Then I remember how keenly the boys in Berlin are learning Swahili verbs, how avidly they're committing to memory the Danish timetables, and I'm afraid that I may not ever be a Roman doctor, after all.

Though I am very much on the right path. I have already learned something very important: medical science is only international in *theory*, in its abstract principles. Beside the sickbed it is very much national. It is therefore right and proper that foreign degrees are not accepted here; this has been driven home to me in the pharmacy much better than if they'd taught it at university and I had graduated *summa cum laude* from the course.

Every treatment is a co-operation between doctor and patient. You can't start by giving the patient a lecture on philosophy. The Italian with a temperature asks for laxatives. Their ear may be inflamed with St Anthony's fire, their neck might be taut with meningitis, but they're angry at their insides and at their doctor who doesn't even know that *qui bene purgat, bene curat - who purges well, cures well.* The pharmacist has numbered a row of drawers from one to ten, which saves him a lot of time when the local women come – "A laxative for a five-year old boy! He's got a rash."

Rashes mean bad blood, and therefore need laxatives. Scabies, as people have known for centuries, is the result of little creatures appearing under the skin because of an unhealthy imbalance of the body's natural fluids. This also requires laxatives. Laxatives are good for spring in general, preferably with a blood-purifying treatment, and therefore we should not be surprised at the fascists' treating people's liberal views – for them, no doubt a sign of sickness – with castor oil.

Inflammation is known – in Galen's phrase – as *calor.* This is the cause of chapping around the mouth, stomach pain, and one of its variants *riscaldo*, or urinary infection. The heart 'whistles slightly' if it's unhealthy. Pleurisy is an unusually dangerous disease. Its muscular pain is caused by the acid from ants, which can be washed away by the use of certain salts. For coughs, you need a syrup. Nervous exhaustion and weakness, which manifest themselves in tiredness and a reduced work-drive (which is to say that they are very common illnesses!), they treat with a restorative cure, with calcium, vitamins and iron given intravenously. Taken orally they would lose their magic properties.

Woe betide anyone who dares challenge these dogmas! People will lose all respect for him, no matter how wise, or snowy-white of beard.

By the end of 1938, sulphonamides had started to appear in the public consciousness too. There were legends surrounding them, for example that egg white would turn the magic powder to poison, and that therefore you should never eat egg-pasta on the same day as your dose of sulphonamides. This mysterious property does wonders for the new drugs' reputation.

The inexperienced doctor will prescribe a medicine, and be surprised when it doesn't work. It never occurred to him that the patient, just to be sure, took it with a dose of laxatives!

I start daring to venture into the laboratory, and establish diplomatic relations with Signorina Maria, the Neapolitan girl. Her face has an air of the Don Quixote-like visage of the Irish poet, though hers is less symmetrical, with a slightly thinner beard. I fail to understand how she can cook up all those recipes in this inordinate mess.

Then I realise. She deals in quantity. I see the following on three enormous jars: Dott. Vacchi, liquid I, liquid II, liquid III. Then two imposing boxes, Dott. M. powder. Dott. M. cream. All in all, there are four doctors working in our neighbourhood, excepting ours, who comes in purely out of professional passion, having handed over his practice to his son long ago. None of them prescribe more than four things – it's easier to prescribe ready treatments, and many drug companies reward the doctors if they issue a certain number of prescriptions for their products. Our Maria makes these sixteen preparations, months in advance. To keep up appearances, the pharmacist nonetheless makes the patient wait a little.

I could happily spend my whole day in the pharmacy. The old man has delegated a few intravenous treatments to me, I'm treating the pharmacist's chronic varicose veins, and I am happy to help Maria pour bicarbonate of soda into little packets. I breathe easier when I step through the door and I even find a certain joy in dragging back a faint odour of camphor with me to my bed.

But I want to read. If a man has eaten and slept, he can easily start to crave for books. It seems that, immersing myself in the world of books, I might find that point that Archimedes found, that quiet place he discovered when the barbarian Roman obliterated his circles in the sand. I want to grab hold of something that is eternal and true. Cabillaud has his faith and his prophecies, but what should I grab on to in the mind-bending whirligig of mosques, whale hunters, the dead of Bligny, cheese-shirts and depressin?

If only I were a mathematician! Maybe somewhere in the cool, distant world of equations there are holy truths and real comforts.

I try and hold on to the stationary stars. Let the end come if it must, let paranoia reign victorious, but let it find my soul light-years away, on distant milky ways. I believe that even without a knowledge of mathematics, I will be able to reach the reassuring limits of human knowledge, and will be able to understand the theory of relativity; just as I understand without calculation what the priests in Salamanca never managed to, that the world is round, and yet we don't all slide off it, that there is no 'up' and 'down'. I believe that the library is another veil between me and the people hunting other people, the five-lira coin forgers, and the floodlights of the Ministry of Propaganda... this is where I want to go and hide.

Tonight I'll go see the prince, and tomorrow I'll go to the library. The twists and turns of history seem to affect Don Agesilao about as much as they do his ancient, armour-suited ancestors. The arrival of the new piano has been the only significant change here for the last thirty (or perhaps a hundred and thirty) years. The music library, though, has grown by three volumes, two concertos by Johann Christian Bach and the four-handed version of Bach's *Kunst der Fuge*.

"I was in luck," says the prince. "This is the latest publication by the German Bach society. There are only two copies in Italy. And the orchestral part of the Johann Christians is transcribed in such a way that it's easy to play on two pianos."

The prince speaks with the passion of the true dilettante. I know that he practices determinedly. There are some people who find their calling at forty – they start to write or to paint, they dedicate themselves to an instrument like a gambler on a losing streak to roulette.

"Johann Christian," I reply, "is on a par with Mozart. Not many people know that he was the conductor of the first orchestra in which only professional musicians were allowed to play, the London Professional Orchestra. It was a big deal in a world where only the Italian singers at the Vienna opera were professional artists. As for the rest, the jockeys of the Spanish Riding School played the horns, the scribes of the court archives played violin and the drums were lent by the watchmen of the Burg. Poor Mozart struggled with them terribly. Haydn's ensemble played to keep the Eszterházys' card games company. When Schubert played for Napoleon, the assembled company merrily carried on chatting. By the time people learned that the way to enjoy music is in silence, with your eyes closed, they were sitting in front of a gramophone."

"Yes, it is interesting, isn't it, that Schubert played for Napoleon. It must have been at Schönbrunn, after the battle of Wagram. It's characteristic of Napoleon's musical taste that he didn't like Méhul. Every time he saw him, although of course he remembered absolutely everybody, he asked him his name. 'Still Méhult, sire,' the composer would reply."

We sit down to play. What a fantastic composer Johann Christian was! It's such a shame that he disappeared in his father's shadow. But there are one or two people who valued him higher than his old man – Johann Sebastian himself, for one. 'My sons,' he writes in one of his letters, 'Christian and Philipp Emmanuel, despite their youth, have already attained my level, and in many ways surpassed me' [*Haben ihres zarten Alters zum Trotz meine Fertigkeiten nicht nur erreciht, sondern dieselben übertroffen*].

"At Christmas, you'll get to meet my sons," the prince says. "They're splendid fellows. They're just as interested in sports as history and natural history. My daughter, too, will be here."

I daren't ask if Diana, since I already know her name, is a ten-year old sapling, a twelve-year old blossom, or a fourteen-year-old stripling.

"Can you come more often this month?"

"I'm at your service."

"Then let's say the day after tomorrow at a quarter past eight."

"With pleasure."

I don't know what to tell Amadeo when he sees me out. Surely I can't tip my creditor?

In the morning, I get up early and go to the pharmacy to tell them that from now on, I'll only be in in the afternoons – my mornings belong to the library.

Following Péter Pogány's directions, I find it right away. You can't miss this castle-like monolith on your way from the Pantheon to the Corso, which rests on its broad base like the one-pound weight on a scale. The Jesuits built it. They were strict with themselves, as well as others – the monolith is incomparably grim and immovable; even its windows look inwards. The fathers spent all their money on the church – the *Gesú*. This was not a place designed for moulding gold, but personalities.

The Italian state confiscated the building, along with the library inside, but the castle kept on moulding personalities. One of its wings became a high school, the other the National Library.

There's a fountain playing in the courtyard, and creeping ivy lining the walls. The immense walls deaden all sound. The very bricks scream silence. If you raise your gaze from the books, it will only alight on more books, and the books are stubbornly silent.

They also stubbornly speak. Rome has fought with them and against them plenty – it was here that the *indexes* were made, it was from here the orders to burn them were promulgated. It is here that books are banned by the Ministry of Propaganda, but Rome is nonetheless the city of books. Many more people visit the books in vellum bindings than their cloth-bound counterparts. Even the banned books have stayed in the very place where they were condemned, waiting – waiting still – for their time to come. One day, the Italian state liberated those who had been condemned by the index. And one fine day, those, too, will be free that now bear the censor's mark on their foreheads. The books that were once in power, the handbooks on witch-burning (like Martin Del Rio's infamous work on the subject from 1609), have retreated in the great silence, as if they had given up once and for all on ever regaining their former place. Little did they know that their time, too, would come again. Here in the National Library, in the treasure-trove of the *Santo Spirito* hospital and in His Holiness' library, the books that survive their bans accumulate and accumulate. There are sharp weapons hidden 'tween the walls of the Jesuits' former castle.

In the long corridor where the catalogues live, I find Péter Pogány. He's busy leafing away.

"How's it going?"

"I've been given a bit of a tough subject."

"What's that?"

"Historical treatments of old-age illness, or in Latin: *Historia medicinae senilitatis, sive medicinae gerocomicae.*"

"Sounds better in Latin."

"I like historical topics, I think I can do it pretty well. Right now, I'm looking for Roger Bacon's 1290 work, *De retartanda senectute,* and if I can find that, I'm on the straight and narrow."

"Is your Latin that good?"

"I told you I studied philology!"

"Yes, and you also promised to introduce me to Italian literature!"

"If you like, we can go get a cappuccino and talk a while. I'm really grateful for any excuse to have a break from my copying work. But I have to get it done, I have to get going!"

"Let's have that coffee – man cannot live by bread alone!"

"What have you read of the Italians?" he asks.

"Nothing, less than nothing."

"No, that can't be right. Have you read *Pinocchio?*"

"Never even heard of it. I did buy a Marinetti book, the *Divisione 28 ottobre.*"

"It's *Tuskó Matyi* in Hungarian."

"Oh, then I have read it. I loved it! Is that Italian? *Pinocchio?*"

"That's right, it's the most Italian book of all."

A scene comes back to me from twenty years before. I suddenly understand something that had always seemed merely strange and incomprehensible. It's as if it happened yesterday...

In 1916, we were holidaying in the Southern Tyrol, in Bruneck. My father was a battery commander not far from there, in St Pauses, and so from time to time, he would come see us and give us a hug. We children even played among the graves of the military cemetery. That cemetery was the apple of some general's eye and he got a platoon of prisoners of war to come every day and plant flowers on the graves, to make wreaths from bark and mosses, and gather up the fallen needles under the spruces. The Italian prisoners of war were usually guarded by an old, bearded, Tyrolean partisan who kept his hands mostly on his pipe and not on his gun. As I sat there one day on a grave, reading Tuskó Matyi's adventures with the Fairy with the Turquoise Hair, one of the Italians came over and glanced at my book. I now remember that he said 'Pinocchio!' 'Not beanochio,' I said, 'it's *Tuskó Matyi*'. Then the Italian pulled his nose, and showed it growing longer and longer, as the puppet's nose would grow when he lied. Then he made donkey's ears, and said 'eeh-ahh!'. I, too, said 'eeh-ahh,' because *Matyi* and his friend turn into donkeys. We understood one another. We ran round and round the grave, going 'eeh-ahh,' and then the Italian leafed through the book, looked at the whale and the fire-eater, and began explaining something very passionately, sighing deeply all the while... and that was 'Pinocchio'!

"There isn't an Italian alive who doesn't know it. And there isn't a single one alive who doesn't in some way resemble Pinocchio. Piniocchio always wants to do the right thing, but never quite has the necessary determination. His conscience is a talking cricket. His dream is the *paese del balocchi*, the land of toys. His greatest fear is the big *carabiniere*. You can't stay angry at him, and he's forever dreaming of the fairy with the turquoise hair. You see, there's only one thing that could save this country, and that would be for Pinocchio himself to march up to the Duce and tell him on behalf of the entire nation that the only –ism really possible in Italy is a universal liberal pinocchinanism."

"I'll certainly re-read it."

"Do you know *Heart*?"

"Yes, of course, and now that I think about it, that's Italian, too."

"Yes, but it's more than that. It's the gateway to Italy. You can only approach any real truth about Italy in a book that has a big red heart on the cover. Don't trust the ones with a boot on the cover. This imperium only extends to the outer membrane of the heart."

"But fascism…"

"I already told you that it isn't really serious. It only touches the surface. It's nothing more than the nation's skin rash. It's an aggressive shirt-fad, a sad plague of symbols. It goes away, comes back perhaps, and then goes away again. It doesn't touch the heart. Read *Heart*, and you'll understand the Italian family. No-one writes love-letters to their brothers and fathers like Italians – and to their mothers, even! The little boy who went *from the Apennines to the Andes*, that's him! Kayserling once said that Italy is a matriarchy, the rule of the mothers. He was almost right – it's actually the cult of the mother that governs society, a sort of domestic cult of the Madonna. The warriors of this cult are the heroes and the poets. There is one treasure here, and only one, that cannot be purloined – a mother's heart. You have to read *Heart* in Italian. In any other language it's some pathetic dream-world. In Italian, it rings true. The real Italy was always dreamlike to any stranger, a little unreal, as if from a fairy-tale, like the Baghdad of the Caliphate. Even its title is untranslatable – you have to have lived here for years before you can fill that dish with true meaning. Do you know who are the real immortals here? The sons of *Heart*. Go out in the street, ask people to name three prime ministers, or three generals from the Great War, or even to name a minister from five years ago – no-one can. But everyone knows the little Savoyard drummer-boy, the Romagnolo bleeding for his grandmother. They're alive, they exist. They're immortal."

"It's by De Amicis, isn't it…"

"Oh, he's a terrible third-rate, thick-headed scribbler, but he really outdid himself! One can apply to this book what Unamuno said about *Don Quixote* after trashing its author: 'It's not his work. He was merely the father – its mother is the nation'. And isn't all honour due to the mother, who laboured for it painfully?"

"So, *Pinocchio* and *Heart*, that's Italian literature?"

"The part that's living. There are other parts, too, but we'll talk about them another time. Come, don't you want to see the card index?"

"Can you show me where it is?"

"Yes, come on, I have some work to do as well."

The index is excellent, and I find the books I'm looking for – Poincaré's *Science et Méthode* and *La Science et l'Hypothése*, both of which I know already, but which I'd like to re-read. Next I want to read James Jeans and Eddington, and then de Broglie and finally Reichenbach's *Philosophie der Zeit und Raumlehre*. I've decided to read as if I were cramming for an exam.

I go see the administrator about a library card. My moustache makes me look older, and they make the *tessera* out for the 'professors' room'. What an eternal city Rome is! The term *tessera* used to be applied to the square metal tokens issued as tickets for the Colosseum back when they were still feeding Christians to the lions. I like these words that have been tripping off the tongue for two thousand years, and yet are still going.

A few days later, it turns out that this pass is a very precious thing indeed – an *entrée* into a rarefied circle.

In the glory days, they were the born VIPs at expensive hotels. They were equally at home in London, on the Riviera, in Constantinople or in the lobby of the Tokatlian hotel. If you didn't know them from there, you could always get to know them on the silver screen. They are the regulars of the great, legendary libraries: the British Library, the Bibliotheca Nazionale, the Library of Congress; their lives exist in that liminal space where the world of books flows into real life. They are the stewards of the love lives of literature. It's through their pen that all those books already written give way to a new, great, work. They are the prospectors of gold who will spend years digging for a little handful of metal. They hunt after people, or their shadows and mirror-images. They are the ones who awaken the dead, the unchangeable guard.

And I was introduced into their company. I found a seat among the living repositories of knowledge.

I was looking for something in Brockhaus's encyclopaedia, some concept, when someone spoke to me:

"Are you foreign?"

"Yes."

"Do you happen to speak Dutch?"

Now, it just so happens that I do not speak Dutch, but I do speak German, English, and a little Swedish. It also happens that my shoes need resoling again, because the inmate who did them last time did not use the finest quality leather. I therefore reply cautiously:

"I'm sure I speak enough to try and help you."

"Oh, that is truly a stroke of luck! My name is Sacco, professor of economics. I need something translated from Dutch, Keesing's *Het ekonomische Evengewicht.*"

"I'm afraid my Italian may not be quite proficient enough…"

"Oh, don't worry about style. I don't want to publish it, I just want to read it. If you find something too hard, you can just write it in English or French. I just want to know what the work says." Then, with the precision one would expect from a professor of economics, he adds, "I could pay five lira a page."

For five lira a page, I can speak Dutch. I can keep my feet dry for a month from two pages alone.

"How many pages is the book?"

"Three hundred, but it's not urgent. If you can do a hundred pages a month and drop them off to me…"

Fifteen hundred lira! Now that I think about it, my Dutch is actually quite good. And if not, there's plenty of dictionaries around. I can do three pages in three hours – which still leaves me time for two or more pages of my own reading. I keep my mornings, from two till five I give myself over to economic equilibrium, from five till seven to blood pressure, from seven till nine, dinner, and from nine till seven a.m., bed. I owe Aldo two hours a week, the odd few hours here and there with the prince... and then I can devote my thoughts to the stationary stars. I can rise above the mists, and fly at the speed of light, I can go round and round the disc of the milky way, I can chase distant solar systems in curved space; and I can look, in inter-galactic infinity, for that kernel of meaning in our world that I – in this tiny speck of Euclidian reality – and many other of my fellow scientists in the library, seek so avidly, and so hopelessly.

Tell the library: I have arrived.

Rome, 1943

Six Years in Rome,
1943

So now it seems that after all this time
the home of poetry, grapes and luscious fruit,
a place that was not offered, nor was mine
has drawn me in and I have put down roots.

And so perhaps, should I be laid to rest
here in my coffin in my dead man's shroud
cypress and yew entwined about my breast
I'll not be a stranger in the alien crowd.

translated by George Szirtes

The historian enters the library with the naïve assumption that he will be able to unravel the mysteries of bygone eras from within. A golden period, a miserable century, always leave behind them a box-full, or a mountain's worth of material. The first, more "innocent", and the second much more thorough, world wars left unimaginable quantities of paper in their wake. These should keep the historians busy for the foreseeable future. Unless, that is, Mars, ashamed of his previous amateur efforts, decides to obliterate the whole lot in his next world war.

The contemporary to an event looks doubtfully into the future at the researcher's job. Only an infinitesimal proportion of events are recorded. Millions of people were turned to ashes or to dust without writing so much as a word of what they saw, wanted, believed, or suffered. With a few exceptions, we are also lacking the memoirs of their executioners. Documents can in no way claim to represent mankind's diary. Even numbers and photographs have learned to lie. Even the actors themselves don masks when ascending the stage of world events. Ministers of the Interior have learned from thieves that it's safer to wear gloves when handling documents, lest an incriminating finger-print be left behind.

Who will tell the stories of today? So much will be lost. Too many people died without testament. Entire libraries went up in flames. Embassies and High Commands destroyed their diaries. Ships sank. Aeroplanes, spies, and millions of children died without leaving so much as their names behind. One or two accidental survivors tell their stories – but to whom? To their forgetful contemporaries? One in a thousand, or in ten thousand, will write their memoirs. And how many of those that do, do it only to try and save themselves, to wash away their sins, to attack and accuse their contemporaries? How many write today merely in order to couch the chaos of the past universal conflict in terms of the perfectability of the future? How many find "our" world merely "background" and "landscape", whose only use is to serve as backdrop to the fictitious narrative or two they decide to locate in it? If the past hurts you, you don't want to remember. If it doesn't hurt, you've already forgotten it, and the people who really experienced it experienced a truly world-shaking catastrophe in its everyday details, while the people who lived far away from it are remote from the shared secret of these millions of people: the spirit of the age.

Many were too young when these things happened, and were still too pre-occupied with their own existence. For others, it was all much of a muchness, their years and illness stood between them and world events. There are very, very few of those who can tell a tale, who can say: this is what I saw, what I heard, this is how it was.

How was it again? How did it all start?

The start was already a continuation. The biographer is lucky in being able to begin with the time and place of his subject's birth, but the narrator telling a story is already lying if he starts "and that's how it all began!" Even in the best-case scenario, he begins just where someone else has left off, saying, "and that's how it all ended". What a wonderful ending it is to be able to say, "and they crowned Franz Josef King of Hungary"! Kufstein, Olmütz, Arad… doesn't matter, all's well that ends well – rejoice and be merry! And what a terrible start it is that "Austro-Hungarian troops crossed the Serbian border." What a lovely ending that the tanks stop in Flanders' poppy fields, and there is peace. What an awful start that Chamberlain negotiates in Godesberg and then turns to his entourage to ask "Do you think Hitler liked me? Did I make a good impression?" We have at our disposal a broad selection from the stockpile of good endings, and the bad starts that followed them as night follows day, but if we really want to say what we have to say, we have to go all the way back to the very beginning of beginnings, to the venerable Homer, who taught us to start our story in its middle, and to leave it to our real, imagined, or adapted hero to tell us how things got to

138

that point. As for the ending, don't let that worry you! Life itself does not close with someone who has accomplished his tasks, made provision for his children, written the final movement of his last symphony. No, it ends with the hero being "taken by the devil," "biting the dust," or to use less florid language, "expiring," or "dying." The story dies when its author puts down his pen. Does he put it down to the strains of the wedding march? At the signing of the peace accord? It doesn't really matter, because events will very soon turn his full-stop into a comma.

So tell me, O Muse, of that fleet of aeroplanes that appeared in the sky above Rome at ten o'clock in the morning on the 7th September, 1943.

In a real epic, the Muse, after saying that it consisted of five hundred Liberators from Sicily, would add that stranger things have happened in the skies over Rome. For starters, but really for starters, Romulus and Remus saw vultures. Before Hannibal's incursion, round fiery shields flashed across the sky. Once, in early Christian Rome, during the black death, when a plague procession was just crossing the bridge before Hadrian's tomb, the Angel of Death appeared above it, and sheathed his sword. Pope Pius XII said (we'll surely get the details at his beatification) that – walking in the gardens of the Vatican – he saw the Sun spinning. And if anyone still doubted the veracity of these events, there is one that they can reach out and touch with their own two hands – the marks of St Peter's knees preserved in the church of *Santa Francesca Romana*, in a corner of the Forum.

The story goes that St Peter was preaching in the Forum, but the people were not paying attention. Their attention was diverted because Simon Magus happened to be flying around above their heads. Needless to say, devils were carrying him on their palms, which is why he flew so confidently, up above the marble fronts of the temples. The crowd, the ignorant crowd... all they cared about was Simon up in the air, while Peter was down on the ground. Until, that is, Peter fell to his knees to beg the Lord to chase away the pack of demons carrying Simon. All of a sudden, the sulphurous devils disappeared, the Magus fell to his death, and St Peter's knee-marks have convinced many a sceptic over the centuries that the skies of Rome do, indeed, harbour miracles.

Having said all of which, it is not strange – merely unusual – that the metal behemoths appeared in the sky, which was bright, though a mite foggy at its edges. It is unusual that somewhere, in the immeasurable distance, a thousand factories had made those ten thousand little parts that – when all assembled – made such a fantastic flying machine. It is unusual that that same God who had recalled the unrepentant Angel of the plague, had several millions years ago, foreseeing this moment, created fish whose oils had slowly turned into petroleum, from which a spark can ignite the heat of the ancient seas, so that many children could be burnt all at once in a Polish field, or that aeroplane engines can be made to turn. It is unusual that modern chemistry should be born out of the alchemists' search for the philosopher's stone and the secret of eternal life, an abstract and unselfish latter-day science which managed to produce, as the happy culmination of a long series of experiments, TNT; and that this high explosive had helped unearth from the Pennsylvanian cliffs the metal army that was now marching above Rome so that it may, using the laws that Galileo codified into Latin words and numbers in this very city, come and descend upon us and turn a quarter of the city (although which quarter, we were in no position to know) into just so much rubble.

By the time the air-raid sirens sounded, the machines were already approaching from the South. The rhythmic ebb and tide of the pounding of their engines was getting closer. People started to run. I was standing up by the obelisk of the *Trinità dei Monti*, and I listened to the sounds in the quiet city long-deserted by cars and carriages, as if I were listening to an organ being repaired. The low C of the bourdon pipe is stuck on the pedal, and there's trouble up there in the third manual, too, but it's hard to isolate the soft, deep, reverberating sound in the multitude of pipes. Should I run? There's no real point, because bombs don't make a difference between "here" and "there" (bombs are strictly undiscriminating on this point). Should I just stand here? It would be a bit odd just to stand still while everyone else was running around, as if I were trying to show off with my courage. Am I really brave? Not at all. They've only bombed Rome twice before, and even then it was the outskirts of town, they may not be aiming for this part of the city. Perhaps the machines will keep going, and this evening the BBC will inform us that the railway station in Florence is ablaze, but that Ghirlandaio's frescoes in the *Santa Maria Novella* remain undamaged. And we will go to sleep in the reassuring knowledge that the German armaments trains have been blown sky-high, and that their reddish glow beautifully illuminates the stained glass enclosed high up in the church's gothic rosettes.

But no. The ground shakes. Just a little, as if a heavy truck had passed behind my back. "It's our turn now," I say to myself and run. There's a friend of mine, a German journalist who lives near here, on the fifth floor of a house in the *Via Gregoriana*, one can see the whole city from there. *Avanti*!

The street slopes, I keep running, and I'm already there. My friend is home, with another journalist and an archaeologist, too. We sit there together as if outside it were merely raining.

The ground shakes. The deep thrum of the engines has been replaced by the quiet rattling of the windowpanes and a deep, not terribly strong, inchoate sound, something akin to a prolonged groaning. It's as if they were pulling a large black curtain up into the air, while little round white clouds puff into the atmosphere, and the pounding of the engines returns.

Becker, the journalist, takes the telescope out onto the balcony and comments: "They're bombing the Tiburtine railway station."

"Nothing of the sort," Hasé replies. "It's the San Lorenzo station. They're carpet bombing it."

"Let's have some tea," Becker replies.

"Let's," we all assent. "Let's go have tea in the study."

Becker shows us his treasures. He opens a tin box and says: "Tea!" He opens another box and points to a bunch of white cubes. "Solid fuel. And I even have water," he says proudly, and puts three cups' worth of water on to boil in a nice little bronze pot.

We sit back down, like the three gentlemen in the opening scene of Ferenc Molnár's *A play in the castle* and are silent for a bit.

I'd like to use this little pause to make my peace with the distant or future reader of these lines. I have no doubt that at this point in my story my reader no longer believes me, having found in my tale some contradictions, and having learned (if by no other means than by reading attentively those consistent detective novels) that there are no contradictions in real life; and that therefore if a suspect contradicts himself during an interrogation, the jig is up: the detective, and justice, have triumphed.

No, I did not lie. I could say that it's the constant (and consciously cynical) lies of the Conan Doyles and the Edgar Wallaces that are at fault. Their logical universe, in which the criminal always finds his noose, is an odd sort of fantasy world, to which not even the revolver can add an air of reality. That my reader was already suspicious when I knocked on Becker's door (yes, knocked, I say, as a fanatical believer in truth, as there had been neither water nor electricity since the last bombing), is entirely the fault of Homer, who forced me to begin my tale *in media res.*

"The Americans are bombing Rome, but the alarm only sounds at the last minute" – don't make me laugh. "The bombs are falling, and these gentlemen are having tea!" – I don't like such cold-blooded heroes. "Tea in the fifth year of the war!" – and where on earth did *that* come from? "And what's someone who listens religiously to the BBC World Service doing with a German journalist as a friend in the first place?" "There weren't too many Hungarians who could walk around the streets of Rome in 1943 unless they were priests or diplomats… and *they* didn't walk around the city much of a morning." "And besides, what does someone who *does* walk around the city in the mornings live off?"

I could continue my story, and tell you that while we were having tea, or more precisely, while we were waiting for the water to boil, the hills of Calabria were home to South African troops, and that the Black soldiers spoke Dutch to each other, while inside Horace's dear *Monte Soratte*, Kesserling was decid-

142

ing the fate of the German armies (when he wasn't too busy listening to his private choir of Don Cossacks, that is); that the pounding engines flew from Sicily to Romania, and that in Rome, in bombed-out Rome, many people looked at each other hopefully and said: "*Avanti!* Long live the enemy!" But I would prefer my future readers not to take this little book of mine and cast it aside. And, knowing that my word of honour is worth only as much as Gulliver's, who vouched for the veracity of the things he saw in Liliput and Brobdingnag with his, I will try to climb out of the pit of my contradictions.

The Americans glide out of the fog and calmly drop the five hundred bombs that turn the outskirts of the city into smoke and flame, laying down their "carpet," then turn and serenely head off towards the sea. The shells of the few anti-aircraft guns burst low, the only potential victims being those who decided to watch the show from their flat rooftops. There is no defence against the bombardment.

None at all. Because states, when they're arming themselves for a coming conflict, usually arm themselves according to the demands of the previous one. The Austro-Hungarian military prepared for war in 1914 so that it would most certainly have won the battle of Königgrätz, had it been fought in 1915. The aerial defences of the Second World War would no doubt have been effective against the bombers of the First. In Germany at the time, they were sticking lengths of paper onto the windowpanes so that the bomb blasts didn't shatter them. Busy little pensioners kept doing this even when eight-tonne behemoths were falling from the sky; and Italy didn't even have any paper strips. Churchill told us that "Mussolini threatened the whole world with an unloaded gun." But he forgot to add that he seriously believed that all the other guns weren't loaded either.

Italian fascism was not gearing up for war. It wasn't gearing up for peace, though, either. It wasn't gearing up for anything, actually, except popular pageants and festivals. Of the Augustinian age, on which it aimed to model itself, it took only the *circens* seriously, because the good, busy people, would take care of their daily bread anyway ("We will give the people sunshine and fresh air!" as the Duce declaimed once from one of his countless balconies).

Fascist politics – and I say this as a contemporary, as a witness, though I will contradict those who seek to understand it from the papers it leaves behind – never even existed. There were big words, speeches, but even the crowd to take them seriously, to give them the slender reality of *creditur ergo est*, was missing.

"Believe, obey, fight!" every Minister of Propaganda declared, but no-one believed. Perhaps because the verb "to believe," like the verb "to love," lacks an effective imperative case, or perhaps because it was hard to find the "credo" among the ten volumes of Mussolini's *Speeches and Writings*, or perhaps because really there was no such thing as fascist doctrine, but merely a group of blackshirted men who one fine day got their hands on the keys to the Treasury. The word "fascist" abroad meant something like "the party of capital". "We are not fascists, we are a workers' party!" the young Goebbels (that "apocalyptic crook") once declared. The fascists liked to call themselves a party of the workers. They liked to fight the figure of the bourgeois, the *borghese* with their single weapon, newsprint; but they didn't like it if the Left started in on the bourgeoisie too, though they may have had more reason to do so. They liked to present themselves among the ranks of the defenders of Western Christian culture. Mussolini was an honorary Knight of Málta (for him, they even waived the necessary aristocratic lineage), and Ciano the Knight of the Order of the Golden Spur (in this one respect only, the equal of Mozart). But a little faction of the party, in their paper, the *Antieuropeo,* attacked and disparaged the ideals of "the West". They called themselves serious, cold realists, and then founded the 'School of Fascist Mysticism'. They stood up for the family and its morals, but the ins and outs of the romantic affairs of Mussolini's daughter were discussed far and wide within the fascist movement, and they took the female P.E. teachers of Orvieto to a boarding school, so they could entertain foreign diplomats. In the space of only twenty years, il DUCE (and who would dare write his name in anything other than capitals?) picked a fight with Greece, shelled Corfu, reinforced colonial rule in Libya, hanged the Arab nationalists, attacked Abyssinia; wanted to establish colonies even as the old ones were lost; made a friendship pact with France and demanded Corsica, Tunis and Djibouti; made peace with the Pope and rattled the sword of Islam (made in Florence); threatened Germany over the *Anschluss*, and then made a "pact of steel" with it; supported Finland against the Russians (at the time of the Molotov-Ribbentrop Treaty), and called this back and forth, the precarious waltz of excuses after the fact, "realpolitik".

And as for military preparedness, it largely reached its pinnacle when Mussolini who – first as a journalist, then as the result of a slight wound inflicted by a badly-made shell in some backwater military exercises, was exempt from military service, and spent the First World War largely in the editorial offices – stuck a heron's feather in his tin hat. Having conquered Abyssinia in a war that pitted machine guns against spears, he declared himself First Marshal of the Empire (lest he be outranked by a proper Sergeant). The diminutive king had a fit when he found out.

The army, the famous eight million bayonets, were still waiting for their sixteen million boots, not to mention other supplies. When the American planes flew over the hills at Albano, Italy had more air marshals than aeroplanes, and more admirals than ships. There was no question of effective defence. The "Italian fleet" last featured in the annals of world history at its pre-war parades. Horthy, the last admiral of the short-lived Austro-Hungarian navy, saw it in the Bay of Naples and thought wistfully of his youth, when he could still fire off a shell or two. Shortly before the outbreak of World War Two, Mussolini showed it off to the Genoese, and then it just disappeared. It disappeared partly because they forgot to explain to the Italian pilots the difference (from above) between an Italian battleship and an enemy one, and so the adventurous men of the air force more than once found themselves bombing their compatriots below. It was especially unfortunate that the aerial defence gunners had itchy trigger fingers. And even Balbo, the bearded air marshal, acted in vain when he threw his general's cap out of the plane so that he could be recognised. By the time the hat hit the ground, the ack-ack fire had already hit the plane. After that, the artillery and the air force had to be put under orders to ask questions first and only fire when they knew who, or what, was flying around.

Thus, when the British fleet appeared one day at Genoa harbour, the lighthouse guard very properly asked them to identify themselves. Which the British admiral did, using his twelve-inch guns. The shelling of the city lasted no more than forty-five minutes, because there is a code that still survives from chivalric times that dictates that this is the maximum time you can shell a city from the sea in a single day (ah, the good old days! Pope Paul V laid down that even the Inquisition could only keep their victims on the rack for an hour a day). But there was no such limit on aerial bombardment, and Naples burnt for days under the hail of ordnance.

It would be exaggerating to say that the Italian people were heroic in the face of these trials. If prayer were at all effective, if Saints Anthony and Januarius were efficient patron saints, Mussolini and his entourage would have died in every air raid amid terrific tortures. But God already knows that it's not good to listen to men's prayers, not even for a moment, because people never stop wishing seven shades of hell and damnation on each other, and so it was that the Duce made it to his lynching alive. But putting teleological arguments aside, the reason Italy bore the bombardment so well is that the pain of Naples and Taranto was not felt in Rome, and the High Command was in Rome. The fate of the country was administered by the ministries spread picturesquely on the seven hills, and their contribution was nothing more than a raft of telegrams left, right, and center, that said: "Believe, Obey, Fight!"

Rome itself was not attacked until the summer of 1943. The wail of the air-raid siren meant nothing more than – as everyone knew, since it was a military secret (the Italians called this a *segreto di Pulcinella*) – that the Allies were bombing Naples. The noise of the streets died down, and people waited for the end of the siren's wailing in doorways, as at other times they would have waited for a shower to pass. They didn't talk poli-

146

tics or war during the air raid alarm, only food or coffee (people never talked of love to strangers, even in peacetime). In other words, the conversations in the doorways consisted mostly of "well, well", and "indeed". There were rumours circulating that said Rome could not be bombed because it was a holy city. This the true Roman had a great deal of difficulty believing. For him, Rome is what it is, in the same way as Paris for a Parisian, and Ferencváros to a native: house, home, hunting-ground. It is more real than sacred.

A holy city. Are its citizens better than the rest? More holy? Funny fact: the holy city has never produced a saint. There was once a blessed priest living in the *Chiesa Nuova*, but he was from Florence. It's true that the Roman Saint Francesca got a halo, but she only received the Holy Spirit after the death of her husband and all her innumerable sons. Saint Brigitte was from Sweden, Benedict Joseph Labré, who lived, slept, begged, and died under the arches of the Colosseum, from France. No, Rome does not have its own saints.

"But even if it's not holy, it's not fascist either,' or so went the reasoning of the average Roman. The British know this too, since they know everything anyway. It's a *segreto di Pulcinella* too that the crowds eagerly applauding under the balcony of the *Palazzo di Venezia* are always composed of the same eight thousand secret policemen. We could add that Rome is not particularly Italian either. In 1870, Italian troops came here as invaders, no-one invited them; and fifty years after the invasion of the redshirts, came the black. What has Rome got to do with this war?

This reasoning got stronger and stronger as the Allies got closer and closer. Enemies? No-one looked on the allies of the last war as enemies. Only the newspapers called them that, branding the Anglo-Saxons a band of Communist Plutocrat Hebrew Democrats. It's possible that the reference is to the king of the underworld, Pluto, with whom they, the legions of light in their black and brown shirts, are now locked in mortal combat… but the newspapers have been in fairyland for some time now. If someone wanted to gauge the spirit of the age, or even find out about what was going on around them from the newspapers, they were lost. The edi-

147

tors churned out long sentences. "It's good that Mussolini has allied with the Germans," the citizen said. "If he'd been allied with the French, he'd be sitting in London now as the head of the Free Italian government and tomorrow they'd ship him back here to us!"

Rome withstood only one bombardment. The next day, it was declared an open city.

"Open city" – what a nice historical concept. The city walls, with their guard towers, are still standing here, but the concept of an "open city" still makes sense. It means that these walls are illusory, their guards have disappeared, and the only people left in uniform are the Swiss Guards. Being an open city meant that the staff of the Ministry of Defence and Naval Affairs went to work in civilian clothes, and that instead of glum men in tin hats, (visibly) more jolly types promenaded on the *Via Veneto*. It meant that German officers entered the portico of the Hotel de Russie in borrowed overcoats – too wide or too tight for them – and old trousers, but nonetheless unmistakable by the spring in their step. The Hotel de Russie had had the TRANSPORT-KOMMANDO sign removed from its front and was having its defiantly pre-war name painted back on it. It meant that they put two camouflage nets on the tanks on the tree-lined Pincian Hill instead of one if they left them overnight.

There was something rather operatic about this transformation – or rather, this change of costume – of the capital of the battling empire. In peacetime, the city had been an endless parade of colourful uniforms. From the lift attendant right up to the admirals, everyone had a dark blue uniform. On Sunday afternoons, the navy and air force officers took their broad, azure sashes out for air on the Corso. Five-year-old boys picked their noses in uniform on the promenade, and schoolchildren wiped their inky fingers into theirs. Fascism made sure that everyone had at least one black shirt, hat with a black bobble, or fez, and the whole of this amazing diversity – with soaring eagles on the buttons, roaring lions on the hats, proud fasces and arrows on the blazers – disappeared within twenty-four hours of the first bombardment (at least in

Rome). German Nazis whispered their *Heil Hitlers* to each other, lest the enemy (their enemy) should overhear.

The second bombing, which came even despite the straw hats, was even more serious than the first. It ruined a busy rail yard.

The Allies either refused to acknowledge the unilateral declaration, or the meaning of this (literal) turncoating was too obvious. The British knew with a surprising precision exactly what was going on in Italy anyway. It is not to be forgotten – and this is the sort of thing the official scribes of history are likely to forget nonetheless – what happened to the great map that the Ministry of Propaganda had erected in the middle of the city at the start of the war, in the *Piazza Colonna*. It was a huge wall-map representing the Mediterranean region. Little flags, arrows, boats, showed the progress of the fascist troops. After the noon update on the state of the war on the radio each day, the fire brigade came racing up, sirens blaring, to push the little toy boats on the map around accordingly. But the goddess of victory is quixotic; they had to sound the retreat in Greece, prisoner-ships left from North Africa for India, the Abyssinians found some guns to replace their spears, and the Italian prince in charge had to start taking his breakfast at the pleasure of a British general. And when a British war correspondent and a photographer somehow lost their way in Somalia and happened upon the Italian army headquarters, the last ten thousand Italian troops stationed there surrendered to them. The firemen no longer came, and the map sat inert at the base of the Roman column which, in its protective concrete covering, seemed now to be so meaninglessly reaching into the sky, like the sole surviving chimney of a bombed-out factory. Weary secret policemen leaned against its walls, waiting for that naïve passer-by who might someday express his views on the current military situation with an arm gesture aimed at the map. The busy readers of the National Library, not far away, quoted Nostradamus: "Weep, Milan, Lucca, and Florence, as your great Duc climbs aboard his carriage, To move the government near Venice, If the Column changes in Rome". But the Romans merely mut-

149

tered to themselves, and eventually the secret police gave up wanting to know who wished what on whom. One day, early in the morning, two huge army trucks arrived at the square in ostentatious silence and in a matter of minutes disassembled, packed, and removed the whole assemblage. Perhaps to save on precious petrol, or perhaps to go on sticking flags on it in the privacy of their own homes...

By nine a.m., London radio had reported the event. And at eleven, as if some great national gathering had been convened, there was a huge crowd gathered on the *Piazza Colonna.*

That's why the "open city" plan didn't work, and that's why the bombers came. Mussolini wasn't around to see them, though, because he was somewhere up north, in conference with Hitler. "In conference"... an expression straight out of the fairy-tale newspaper world. In reality, he sat mute in front of the Führer, who would brook no interruption, and tried to decipher the meaning of the torrent of words. But it was too late, too late to learn German, too late to admit that he didn't understand, too late to jump ship, and too late to build up Rome's air defences.

Five days later, he was toppled. The "Great Council" of his party, like in one of those much-maligned democracies, ousted him unanimously. Maybe there is some truth in those detective stories after all – the killer is rumbled because he missed one, apparently insignificant, detail. The citizens have been disenfranchised for some time. The gathering of black-shirts that was laughingly called a parliament did nothing more than get together to sing patriotic songs. But a few dignitaries, and some of the newly-minted counts, like Grandi and Ciano, some senile marshals like De Bono, could finally, for once, agree on something.

The DUCE (or maybe that upper case was meaningless all along?) disappeared. But something resembling a state still remained. There was a king, a prime minister, a bureaucracy, and even a motto (made up of three words): *La Guerra continua – the war goes on.*

That's why the bombers came the third time, that's why the sirens sounded late, and that's why there was no air defence save one or two German guns along the railway.

150

That we – as foreigners – were calmly sitting sipping our tea? Even thinking back on it now, I can't bring myself to feel scared. Fear is not an *idée fixe*. Someone who's afraid knows what he's afraid of. In a dictatorship there is a monopoly on fear, like there is on salt, or tobacco, and it belongs to the police. There is only this murderous body to be afraid of, that perverts the words of the law, shreds nerves and drills teeth. They knock on the door and take people to suffer and die by night. They shut off a street, round the people up and then break someone's head because he expressed the view that dictatorship is not the best possible form of government, or that the American army is powerful. The police are people too. There are upstanding heads of families among them, willing to serve whatever political system comes along, ready – at a word from higher up – to dispose of their current boss. Compared to them, the carpet bombing is an act of charity. TNT bears no ill-will. We can sip our tea in peace.

We drank tea, because there was tea. The warm, brown tea was exciting, because it came from a far-off democracy. Finding tea was a discipline in itself, whose ins and outs we used eagerly to discuss. I can perfectly understand that the United States – the same United States that recently sat back and watched France's Calvary – came at once to arms the moment Britain had to raise the duties on tea. It's easier to hope with a cup of tea. And Rome is a happy hunting-ground. There are many tea-drinkers here, so people are happy to smuggle it. It simply isn't true that people are constantly concerned with the big questions, that the people hang on the leader's or high-priest's every word religiously. The people want to eat, drink, sleep well, and wish from the bottom of their hearts that the state would take a little less interest in them. The tea-smugglers know far better what the people want than the professors of the "School of Fascist Mysticism." And the good Lord, in his aforementioned foresight, designed the mountain range on the Swiss border in such a way that good things could still get through to the people who had good money to pay for them.

Many things come to Italy via Switzerland, including good news. This is accurately reported in the Swiss press, which signals its independence with the occasional addition of a small sentence beginning "on the other hand", or "notwithstanding" to the bare facts. A little tea, coffee, pepper, cinnamon, cloves – these are seemingly unimportant things that one would think were the last thing on the minds of people going hungry, but they're symbolic – the edible symbols of peace, international trade, and the brotherhood of man. The Swiss border with Italy is almost unpoliced (in the direction of Italy, that is), and there has been only one border incident, when some Italian troops retreating from Greece were greeted by border signs in Greek letters put up by some playful Swiss. "On the other hand" (or "notwithstanding"), only the border with Germany is strictly closed, not to guard against smugglers, but against refugees. The Helvetian Confederation took the view that Hitler's victims were not political refugees, since there were no legal proceedings against them, and so they – on the basis of some finely-worded laws on vagrancy – calmly handed even those people back to the Germans who actually made it over the border. They then got to watch the Gestapo shoot them on the spot. After that, they put up a barbed-wire fence to close the border off completely...

Tea comes in through the Vatican as well. The Vatican is not the Church, but a state. The Church knows no borders. The borders of the Vatican are policed. The Church is looking for souls: *Da mihi animas, cetera tolle tibi* [Give me the souls and you can keep the rest]. The Vatican has a postal service, printing press, and bank: the Bank of the Holy Spirit, whose official language is Latin, and says of itself (also in Latin): *Quidquid ad rationes in re nummaria spectat quae cuique cum externis intercedunt nationibus ligitime curat et exsequitur*. Or, in plain English, it is the lawful organiser and executor of all financial transactions with foreign states. The Church – the *Ecclesia militans* – fights. The Vatican is strictly neutral. The story goes that one dark night the Archangel Michael happened to meet Satan himself in St Peter's square. They went at each other wildly. The Evil One got the Archangel by the throat, and started to strangle him. "Help!" he cried, "help me, Holy Father, help, help!". At last, with all this din, a window on the square opened, a prelate leaned out, smiling benevolently, and said:

'*Non possumus*! You must admit, my dear Archangel, that such an intervention would violate our neutrality,' and calmly closed the window.

"Vatican tea?" I ask Becker.

"Yes, I got a packet of genuine Lyons tea from Weizsäcker, the press secretary. He buys it at the bar. Do you know the bar in the Vatican?"

"Yes, I used to go there when I was doing some research in their library."

"It's such a good place, so pretty. A museum of peacetime. French chartreuse, Danish cherry brandy, Brazilian coffee, Hungarian wines. The Church is truly universal. God, what a wonderful thing is peace!"

A resounding thud outside choruses an affirmative.

"It must be another munitions train," Hasé says.

"I don't think so," says Becker. "Usually, they don't go up all at once like that, but car by car. They sound more like fireworks, a series of smaller explosions one after the other."

The windows rattled once more.

"Maybe it was a munitions train after all. More tea?"

I'm happy to be drinking tea, to be chatting with the German journalist, and the strangers I meet here. They're good people.

Good? Is there such a thing as good people and bad people? Only someone who's lived in a dictatorship can answer that question. Living under fascism is squalid and hopeless, but it does have one very significant advantage – it makes it possible to judge your fellow man according to that very simple classification that the great artists used when they committed the Final Judgement to a wall. On one side are the good, soaring away, on the other side, the bad falling to their damnation. In a dictatorship, this translates as, whoever shares your sincere desire to see the dictator strung up, is good, and anyone who would extend him a sponge soaked in vinegar, is bad. Modern psychology has introduced untold complications into the relations between men. It's become terribly difficult to know who has true worth, and who does not. The lazy crook turns out merely to be inhibited. The poor executioner is a tortured sadist, the bent and miserly usurer is merely neurotic, and in

153

the end we all fall victim to these people whose sins are so completely forgiven by the psychologist. Dictatorship all at once restores the former states in which someone was "brave and honourable", or "low and miserable".

All you have to get clear is who's good and who's bad, and this is not a question of morality, but something entirely different. In case anyone who has never lived in a state dominated by its secret police doesn't understand this, I suggest they go out and mix the (otherwise identical-looking) populations of two anthills, and note how quickly the unreasoning insect sorts out one community from the other.

You can tell someone's sympathies from symbols, gestures, where the emphasis falls in the stories they tell, the station their radio is tuned to, scraps of newsprint, little sighs; from the books they cite, the way their eyes gleam or lament when certain names are mentioned, a word underlined here and there, an exclamation mark. Changes of mind exist only in the "official" histories. In reality, whatever happens politically – whether the tyrant demi-god stays or goes to prison – the good stay good and the bad stay bad. In Rome, I came to understand what the Catholic Church preaches – that you are assigned to heaven or hell for ever, that there is no transition between the two and no mercy, not even after an eternity of millennia.

To err is human. In other words, it can happen that someone gets taken in by an informer, or an agent of the OVRA, but they get taken straight to hell. They once sent someone, for a single careless word, to Lampedusa for ten years, the island with the cells where at high tide the sea came up to the foot of your bed. 'Public opinion' heartily approved the black-shirted Führer's *lettres de cachet*, keeping what they really thought carefully to themselves, knowing full well that anyone who dared speak out about them would immediately be branded a Communist. The rule was that you only spoke after you had felt people out, like an ant, and you always knew who you could, and could not, talk to.

When Mussolini finally fell, and in the belief that his secret police had fallen with him, everyone suddenly revealed themselves. But then Badolgio, the new head of state said *"La Guerra continua*", and people, like the late revellers at a masked ball when the masks have slipped and come off, uttered a tired and faded sigh, and put the masks that hid their true feelings back on.

As for the German journalists, though card-carrying members of the Nazi party I had no doubt, they didn't belong to the paranoid vintage. Nazism, like other epidemics that paralysed children, attacked particular classes. In Austria, it was the class of 1913 and after that went crazy. But the first four years of the war tore masses of these idealists to shreds. And after Stalingrad, even the opportunists – the backbone and basis of Hitler's rule – fell away. The German Romantics who in 1938 were looking for their blue flower in their guard's uniform in Dachau, by 1943 were dreaming of an attempt on Hitler's life.

My two Germans were only concerned, from the very start, with how they could best hide themselves, where best to lay low, get lost, vanish into thin air; they very correctly realised that the very best place was the Ministry of Propaganda.

This also sounds like a contradiction, but it's true. Even in Rome, the people who lived most safely were the ones who took shelter in the shadow of Party Headquarters. The secret police didn't sniff around there so much. It was easy to keep quiet among the screaming little Goebbelses of the propaganda machine. Writers and artists were considered eccentric anyway, and the authorities were lenient with them. Officially, Becker was in Rome to write art historical pieces in order to maintain German-Italian relations. Hasé, who was studying architecture and spoke Italian, had the economic reports he was supposed to send home written by a friend of mine from Vienna. It was he, Eckstein, that introduced us.

"They're good people," he said. These good people are now sitting in Rome with a good, safe plan. They're waiting for the Allied armies, and a chance to disappear before the organised German retreat. "In two weeks, they'll be here", they thought. "We'll disappear before then."

Their plan is nowhere near as original as they think. Too many people are tired of retreating to the tune of slogans of victory. There's even a name for their condition – the soldiers call it "Canada fever".

To disappear! Can you really disappear in a totalitarian state where every gatekeeper is an enemy, an informer, a shake-down artist? Can you disappear in a place where after twenty years of fascism there is no bread without coupons, and no meat even with them? Can you do it in the teeth of the Questura, the militias, the military police, SS, Gestapo, spies and a dozen other similar outfits?

It's a difficult question, and the answer depends on who you ask. If fifty times a hundred thousand people could rise up from the Polish soil, or from under the snows of Russia, they would tell you "no". If eighty times that number could speak from their graves, they would also tell you "no". It's a given fact that dictatorships are a disease, one that kills – and the only thing that's changed from the tyrants of Syracuse to the South American generals with the Napoleon complexes, are the tools at their disposal for murder. But there are exceptions, and their pedigree goes back as far as the dictators' – the fugitive galley-slaves, the escapees from the Bastille, the Blacks who made it to Lincoln's army, the Hungarian peasants who fled through all of China in the First World War, say "yes".

There is no universal solution – no solution for the masses, but there are individual ones. And while the rules are falling into disarray, the exceptions speak for themselves, and – as these lines themselves show – write, scream, speak to those who are in danger, or will be.

You can escape. Sometimes blind luck, sometimes the rules of probability will save someone. The cruiser *Hood* went down with two thousand five hundred souls, and on the edges of the enormous dust cloud swam three survivors without a scratch. But that is the exception to the exception. The rules of the exception are that only those braver than the rest will make it. For someone to disappear, to hide, to cross a border, takes more courage than to stay and howl with the pack. Since we're on the topic of the drowned and the saved, there was a moment when life on deck in a fur coat was more attractive than life in the icy sea in their underwear. "Stay calm, there's no danger," the captain said, and that was the "official version". But the only survivors were those who threw themselves into the icy deep in time. The mass of people went down with the ship.

The people who are swimming in the cold and dark are not yet saved, but they have their own ideas. They see things differently. They may even become a little heartless when they look back at the sinking ship and think "you should have jumped".

The cold and the dark are not symbolic. They are the reality of those who jumped off the deck in '38 and were still alive in '43. There was a terrifying force in this reality, a terror that constricted the arteries. The people paddling in the dark recognised each other and shouted across to one another. It was a bad time to be paddling in the dark when Pétain's police rounded up refugees at the Andorran border to hand them over to the Germans, when the Swiss, with their vagrancy laws, gathered them up and handed them back to their executioners, when the Vatican officially told the Vichy government that they had no moral objection to the deportation of the French Jews, and when the Prime Minister of Hungary shot himself in shame at having to violate the terms of the agreement with Yugoslavia.

But there were good moments too. Once, we were listening to the BBC with Eckstein (the Danish broadcast wasn't blocked). In our excitement our Danish improved dramatically. I can well understand the Pentecostal miracle that befell the evangelists, since we listened to the important events of the day in Icelandic, Romanian, Portuguese and Luxemburgish, and somehow understood them. The news said that a large German troop convoy was aflame in the Mediterranean. Thirty thousand people were surrounded by the burning waves, because a tanker had been torpedoed. The people could do nothing but jump from the burning ships into the fiery sea.

Eckstein commented: "You see, that's what you get for having all your papers in order. Do you know how hard it is to get onto a transport like that? How many papers, orders, permissions you need? Those people swimming around in the sea have all the necessary paperwork to try and stick their noses out of the water somewhere they won't get burned off!"

My sole lifeline has for some time been a single piece of paper from the Embassy of the Kingdom of Hungary in Rome, which says that my passport is with the Consulate to be renewed. It is clutching this precarious shield that I contemplate the two Germans making their plans to jump out of certain danger into the deep unknown.

If I have managed to assuage your – very reasonable – doubts, perhaps you will now permit me to return to our little tea-party, at which the cups – understudying as seismometers – occasionally rattle.

"The situation…" says Becker.

"The situation," the archaeologist takes up, "is remarkably simple. It is exactly the same as the Second Punic War, and I would say that we are just before the Battle of Zama. The situation of Germany after World War One corresponded precisely with the situation after the First Punic War. Hannibal's sudden assault through Spain corresponds to the Polish campaign. The British defeat at Dunkirk and the subsequent emotional state of England is the equivalent of the bloodbath at Cannae and *"Hannibal ante portas."* 'We shall fight in the hills,' said Churchill Maximus Cunctator. And I picture Göring as the cavalry general in the Punic wars telling Hitler "you can win, my Führer, but you can't make good your victory," and "if you'd crossed the Channel after Dunkirk, you would have been lunching in Buckingham Palace within a week!". But I tell you this, Scipio is already in Africa, and the legions will be camping in Berlin before long!"

"The situation," Becker says again, in his evident determination to halt the conversation's ancient turn, "has never been as grotesque as it is today. Italy simply doesn't know what it wants. They've locked up Mussolini, and if the cook at our consulate wasn't sleeping with one of the *carabinieri* guarding him, we wouldn't even know which hotel he's playing solitaire in. The fascist party is not banned, but doesn't exist. They haven't released the political prisoners, but they've stopped locking them up."

"Badoglio is having people arrested *en masse,*" I say.

"Yes, but it's not the same. He's not doing it for political reasons. The curfew's at seven, and if someone has a stomach-ache at half past and runs out to the pharmacy, they get fifteen years. That's martial law. He doesn't care what the guy with the stomach ache *thinks*."

"Carthage will fall," the archaeologist says, picking up his former monologue, "but it will fight to the last infant. Its fall will not change the history of the world one jot. The question then, was really whether it would be the Africans or the Latins who would adopt Greek culture."

"I don't understand Badolgio," says Becker. "A curfew is all well and good, but what else is he doing? It's been a month that he's ruled the roost in Italy, why hasn't he surrendered? Is he waiting for the Americans to arrive? Just now, he sent Guerilia up to Treviso to meet with Ribbentrop and assure him that Italy will fight on. With what?"

"Is he negotiating?" Hasé asks. "Maybe the American bombing is just a way of speeding up the diplomatic process. TNT today is as much part of diplomacy as a knowledge of French used to be."

"You mean we can expect peace any day now. The diplomats blather, but bombs talk," I say.

A long blast, far nearer this time than the others, seems to reinforce this. Becker suddenly goes white. Then he remembers himself, and feels he ought to explain his worried expression:

"When I was last in Sicily, in the good old days back when we were bombing Malta, the Brits came up with a new mode of attack. Their bomber groups simply followed our returning bombers back to base, and so there was no question of the air raid sirens being sounded; and when the Junkerses landed, they started dropping their bombs. I was standing at the edge of the airfield when the first wave arrived, and I hadn't a clue what was going on. Fortunately, someone gave me a tremendous kick in the backside, I fell over, and rolled into the ditch at the edge of the field. Fortunately, because at that moment a shower of dirt and shrapnel swept over where I had been standing. It was all over in thirty seconds, and then I stood up to thank whoever had saved my life by his quick thinking."

"And?"

"And it was a boot with a leg still in it. That's what had hit me from behind. It was the posthumous act of an anonymous benefactor. I owe my life to an unknown boot." Turning to the archaeologist, he added, "I don't think that sort of thing happened during the Second Punic War."

But the archaeologist is not offended, and is in fact rather pleased to be able to get back to the ancient world.

"As regards weaponry, it would be easy to draw a parallel between the heavy but very easily manoeuvrable modern tanks and Hannibal's elephants. The initial successes were in both cases attributable to the new weapons."

The air raid siren unexpectedly falls silent.

I have to go, because despite Badoglio, Hannibal, and world history, I still have to solve the central problem of the day: I have to find something to eat, buy it, and take it home, where Diana is waiting for me, expecting me to bring something home from the hunt.

Mechanised war has taken human experience back to its primitive forms. The problems the modern city-dweller faces are on the level of the stone age. Each morning, the men would emerge from their caves and go hunting. Day after day, they had to find their prey, catch it, find a way of cooking it, and then, in the evening seal up the door of the cave so that the wild animals couldn't get in. Each process was potentially fatal, and hunger was ever-present. The need to find food was in the soul, the flesh, and the blood, day and night. The hungry caveman resented everyone who had something to eat. He would concoct murderous, wild schemes to get his hands on a cupful of oil. If he found a morsel of food, he would hide himself to eat it, stuff himself greedily, lick the plate and would try not to think about that moment when the feeling of post-prandial satisfaction would give way to the hunger before the next meal, when the baying wolf in his innards would once more awake. At night, he would search his cave, looking for lost scraps under the table, would chew the cabbage heart he had discarded at noon, and would ransack the drawers if he remembered that there must be one or two sweets left over somewhere from Christmas-time.

Tea-time, conversation, and the daily look into the crystal ball were mere episodes in our private war against hunger. Even the fear of death struggled in vain to dominate the soul in the face of hunger. It would win for a few minutes, and then lose again for weeks.

At the very moment when the air raid sirens fell silent, those Romans who were not lying under some errant corner of the carpet that had been dropped, slightly askew, from the sky, were already thinking about the necessity of finding some lunch.

Of course, moral law dictated that we should have rushed to the San Lorenzo district to help dig out the dead from under the ruins and rebury those the bombardment had turned out of their graves. But moral law was clearly formulated after lunch, and applies only to the world in its well-fed state. I for one sincerely doubt that a man who was truly hungry, who had been going hungry for months, would ever set in stone a childish statement like "thou shalt not steal", or "thou shalt not covet thy neighbour's ass". Also, you needn't bother to forbid hungry men from fornicating. They aren't thinking about anything other than to be full, just once, and don't give a tinker's cuss what the rules governing the world of the well-fed are.

Heroclitus was wrong. He thought that everyone who was awake shared a common world, while everyone who was dreaming was in a separate world all his own. But we don't live in one common world, but in countless separate ones. All our troubles, misunderstandings and conflicts come from trying to transpose the rules of one of these worlds into another, where they are received with blank incomprehension.

In the eyes of the Capucin monk, the history of the world is just an illusion and reality is the devil, God, judgement and the everlasting. For a general, the monk is a crazy civilian, living in a dream-world, praying to that illiterate Jesus who was nothing but trouble, because he turned up in Jerusalem to clear up some murky affair to do with a stolen apple. If you ask a mathematician, he will say that both of them are concerned with immaterial things, because the truth is only to be found in numbers. The psychologist will prove to you that all three are mad, and the man who is yet to eat will laugh at all four, because he's learned that reality is soup, meat, and a little bit of warm pasta, and that the curiosity and accomplishments

161

of the spirit are nothing but a dream of the post-luncheon world, the *mundus postprandialis*, and that these can quickly – and oh so easily! – evaporate into nothing at all.

I go out into the city, back to the Spanish Steps, where you can see all along the mediaeval and baroque parts of town all the way to the dome of St Peter's (or the Mammary of the Mother Church, as someone once said), and I look out over the sea of houses. It's lying before me as if nothing had happened.

I don't know what wounded cities did during the Second World War. Rome didn't move an inch. And there you have the multitude and diversity of the interweaving separate worlds: the bombardment of Rome toppled Mussolini, burnt twenty years of his speechifying in a single afternoon, nullified Italy's ambitions to be a Great Power (the dream of Cavour and D'Annunzio), but Rome, the Eternal City, the *Urbs*, didn't even notice. Whether it was multi-coloured officers or starving civilians who roamed her streets really didn't make an ounce of difference viewed from the perspective of two thousand seven hundred years. One of her basilicas may well have been injured this afternoon, but on her pride there was no stain. There was no hullaballoo of ambulances, firemen, or police. Only people concerned with their lunch proceeded with quickened steps, to make up for lost time. I, too, hastened my pace descending the groups of thirteen steps to Bernini's ship-shaped fountain, and from there straight along the Via Condotti to the very oldest houses.

If reality – reality with a capital "R" – consists of countless little independent realities separated from each other by vacuums of empty space, Rome is the single, united and indivisible mass of countless separate lives and atmospheres. There used to be forests and swamps in between the seven hills. They have left behind the boundaries between them, which the true Roman won't cross. To cross the city... is something only for tourists, whether they be Chinese or Neapolitan. The Roman lives in his little neighbourhood, *nel rione*, where his doctor, his pharmacy, his secret flour dealer are, and where the local policeman will come and tell him when to disappear because he's been denounced. It's the solidarity of the little *riones* that breaks the back of dictatorship. They are the places that keep their mood over half a millennium. In the old Rome, they used to call the city blocks *insula*, islands, and even today the ancient, real, Rome is a city of little islands, like Venice.

I lived in my little *rione* named after the bridge for four years, in an ancient brick castle. That's where I learned Italian, where I learned to cook over hot coals, where I found the pharmacy and started out on my medical career as a taker of blood-pressure; it's where Figaro, my trusted barber (who knows everything) is, and my black market on the *Tor di Nona*. It's a famous street and I'm proud to spread its fame. It was the prison where Giordano Bruno was kept, from where they took him to the stake during the carnival of 1600, held to make up for the cancelled Shrove Tuesday celebrations. It was here that the magician Don Quixote talks about ascended on his fire-breathing horse, when he and his trusty Sancho are sitting blindfold on the wooden horse... and Sancho Panza's wisdom rings in my mind every time I pass by – 'the body cannot support the burden of arms without being properly fed'. Acting here on this ancient observation, they are now selling cornflour from battered tin vats, animals of uncertain origin creatively labelled rabbits, and bones with tiny scraps of fat clinging to them, referred to simply as "venison". This is where you can come and buy charcoal without a ration-book, worth its weight in gold. *Via Condotti* starts off in the twentieth century, but it leads into the timeless, fantastic world of torches, magicians and black-marketeers.

There's no such thing as Rome, only Romes. They are little cities independent of each other in time, space, and feeling; and even if you know one, you are still a stranger in all the others. There is a modern, new Rome, built on new hills. With its white apartment blocks, villas, and cypresses, it looks the way the Central European imagines South America. Its inhabitants like living in the twentieth century. If they play an instrument, it's the gramophone; when they drink, they drink the heirs of wine – grappa and liqueurs; they're searching for a lifestyle. It's no longer fashionable to look to the French; they are awed by the Germans but detest them, and they dislike the English because the very sight of them gives them an acute inferiority complex. So, as they walk along the *Via Veneto* and take their rest in the cafés without coffee, they're waiting for the Americans, their saviours. They will bring them the lifestyle that is easy to adopt, because it's modern, *chic*, and doesn't require too much effort. These elegant prettyboys and their female counterparts, known as '*ga-gas*', know only the very beginning of the *Via Condotti*. That's where they buy their jewellery and ties.

There is also an official Rome – the city of countless ministries. The Ministry of African Affairs employs five thousand essential staff, despite the loss of Africa, not including the monopoly on bananas because that is a huge organisation of its own. There's an overgrown Ministry of the Air, on which stone eagles sit in rows, and which cost so much to build that there was no money left to buy aeroplanes. There's a Ministry of the Interior which employs three hundred thousand people, and a pretty old Naval Ministry overlooking the Tiber (so that it shouldn't entirely forget the sight of water); there's two giant metal cats guarding its entrance, glorious remnants of the Austro-Hungarian fleet. The myriad minions of the multitudinous ministries, allergic as they are to work, all live in Rome, too – the higher echelons Northern Italian, the concierges Southern, and the policemen Sicilian... but their children speak the Roman dialect. They hardly even know the *Via Condotti* exists.

There's a sacred Rome, on the Vatican Hill (which, in Cicero's time was famous only for its bad wine), and in a thousand other places. In twenty or thirty thousand rooms – a hundred disparate worlds which from time to time come together to receive the blessing of a *single* pope. Catholic Rome also has ministries, which hardly differ, with their statistics, computers, and the telephones on the desks of the middle-management, from the headquarters of a large international conglomerate. The bank, the Bank of the Holy Spirit, the *Banco di Santo Spirito*, is just like all the other big banks, except that – unlike them – it is not subject to foreign currency controls. Sacred Rome extends to the ascetic self-mortification of the Trappist monks, the silence of the Carthusians, and includes the enormous world of the seminaries, where the age-old merciless walls guard the young men in their ward, in the very places where countless young men just like them lived before, and where today's generation relive their experiences and struggle with the same insoluble questions, which lead them to the same secret mysteries. There are catacombs and libraries, mendicant friars and prosperous nuns; the cloistered girls of the *Sacré Coeur*, who are not even allowed to whisper together in pairs, but must stand in groups of three on their breaks, alien Scots somehow left behind, and French prelates who are in their heart of hearts atheists; not to mention the fantastically zealous little old Swedish or Jewish ladies who have adopted the Catholic faith. Of this boundless and bottomless sea of religious life, one or two nondescript churches and the palace of the Grand Master of the Knights of Malta overlook the *Via Condotti*.

The visitor knows only the start of *Via Condotti*. That's where the Café Greco has been exuding the aroma of ground coffee for the last two hundred years, where everyone from Goethe to Rabindranath Tagore, from Samuel Morse to Humperdinck, and Turgenyev to D'Annunzio and Buffallo Bill sat and pondered; everyone who was anyone in Rome, had things to sit and think about, and could afford the price of a cup of the black stuff. Whoever writes their name in the guestbook here will never disappear in the merciless depths of history. A little gleam of poetry has blessed their countenance.

But Rome, my real Rome of the many other Romes, starts at the other end of *Via Condotti*. Here, the noises of the other Romes die away. The light reflected from the ancient yellow walls changes the appearance of the passers-by. The piercing noonday summer sun does not penetrate into the narrow streets, the cold winds of winter break on the sharp corners that separate the alleyways. Here, the stairs are steep, the rooms are floored in stone, and the doorhandles are as worn as St Peter's toes. This is the ancient town of the princes, the coachmen, the innkeepers, shrines and brothels. The only, the true Rome! It was here when the *bersaglieri* with the feathers in their hats shot a hole in the city walls near the *Porta Pia*;

it was still here when the blackshirts with their cudgels and their castor oil, their triangular death's-heads flags rattled in through the unguarded portals. The *palazzi* are patient – there's prince Lancelotti's palace (he's the one who delivers the Golden Rose to virtuous Catholic queens, and it's hardly his fault if he only has work to do once a century...) on the corner of the *Tor di Nona*. When the Italians came, he had his gates sealed, declaring that while the Pope was a prisoner in the Vatican, he would use only the back door.... This is where the ancient mansions of the *Massimo*s, the *Giordano*s and the *Doria*s sit gathering their patina of age. The princes do not belong to the population of "modern" Rome – their charming dialect is more akin to that of the coachmen and grocers. The latter do not curtsey before the great and the good, but rather converse with them in the full knowledge of their dignity as men.

It's perfectly natural – the nobles and the commoners lived in these palaces for centuries side by side, and so how could they not grow into one? Their children played together, sometimes even beyond puberty. They bled together in the sword and halberd battles of the feudal age. Now, they curse the twentieth year of the dictatorship together. That the princes have remained princes and that the coachmen have, at most, become chauffeurs, is also a perfectly natural Roman tradition. In Imperial Rome, a thousand years after the city was founded, people still knew who was the son of patricians, and who of plebeians – a language, fate, and millennium in common could never change *that*. But this was each person's private affair – to the outsider, both were Roman citizens.

Even (especially!) during the famine, when finding sustenance began to resemble hunting again, it was difficult to forget Rome's historical contributions to culinary culture. Gastronomic traditions here were sacred, and as the breviary sets out the prayers for every day in every season, so there is an iron rule that says that the year starts with pig's trotters and lentils, continues on St Joseph's day with pastries, and lamb at Easter, then peas and eels in late spring, and artichokes in summer, with almond sweets on All Souls'. And each gastronomic year is made up of fifty-two gastronomic weeks, with gnocchi on

Thursdays, cod on Fridays, tripe on Saturdays. Rome, the old, traditional Rome, is the city of rules and order, and rules and order extend strictly to smells and flavours, too. It took a conflict that engulfed the world for this order to be breached; the city's abandoned stoves waited for the Angel of Peace to appear above the *Castel Sant'Angelo*, to sheath his sword and pronounce the sacred words: *giovedi gnocchi, sabato trippa,* and may it forever be thus, *omnia saecula saeculorum.*

Beyond the end of the *Via Condotti*, the little churches hardly extend above the little houses. The house of God stands peacefully shoulder to shoulder with the houses of men, and both cohabit just as peacefully with the houses of ill-repute. These are anyway only distinguished by the chains across their shutters. The enemy of religion is not secret passion, but dispassionate intellect. More than a few of the streets of old Rome were paved, among them my own street, the Street of Baboons, with the taxes levied on the brothels, and not even the dictatorship could close these hallowed patrician establishments: their founding documents were signed and sealed by the chancellor of the Papal States, and the Italian state undertook at the peace treaty of Villa Albano and then again in the Lateran Accords, to respect all papal patents. And therefore what could be further from these respectable institutions than the concept of sin? They open at ten a.m. like the shops, and close at ten at night, so that the girls can get a good night's sleep, and in the long-gone days of peace, they used to serve bean soup to boot, because the privates on their Sunday afternoon leave didn't have enough time to go somewhere else to eat. The kindly matron at the door would ask the soldiers, "would you like the young lady with soup, or *au naturel?*"

It's hardly sacrilegious that in the street of the rosary makers, the *Via dei Coronari*, the houses with their chained shutters are ranged one after the other – more anachronistic, if anything. But isn't it just as anachronistic that here you also find the church of *Santa Maria della Pace* – the Virgin of Peace, where the candlelit procession came in vain when the Germans crossed the Marne? Isn't everything that's immortal anachronistic?

That was certainly how Mussolini saw it. "I hate picturesque Italy!" he declaimed (he acquired his habit for lapidary statements from Emil Ludwig's book on Napoleon), before letting slip the pickaxes on the old Rome. The Romans looked on powerless, furious, inconsolable, as the ancient streets around the Colosseum disappeared, then the city-wall-like rows of houses leading up to the Capitoline Hill, and how the centuries-old mass of vaulted buildings and little fountains in the Borgo made way for a blank desert, only daring to protest when the Duce, in another of his fits of enthusiasm (*voglio far tabula rasa con tutto quello che si chiama civiltá umana – I want to wipe away all that is so-called human civilisation*), wanted to demolish the *Piazza Navona*. Not all dictators are the same, and Mussolini, who in his fits of depression played gruelling romantic airs on his fiddle, could sometimes be prevailed upon. He would occasionally reconstruct (on the basis of the old plans) what he had demolished, and so it is that the street of the rosary makers and the little alleys it gives birth to have survived to this day. And so it's understandable that the residents here hate not the Americans, who bomb outlying railway-yards, but the man who spent twenty years demolishing their city.

I still have time to go see my barber, in his rented space under one of the street's arches. I've gotten used to dropping in on him whenever I pass this way. There were days when my sole moment of pleasure was when I could bury my face in the hot towels after he had finished shaving me. Figaro (I call him that because I never learned his real name) is one of the "good people", perhaps even of the best.

"Well," I ask from the door, "what news?"

"Nothing bad," he replies.

Then I notice that he still has a visitor. I shoot Figaro a conspiratorial glance.

"You can talk. He's one of us," he says.

"I'm small, but clever," the stranger says, by way of introduction, and since I can see that at least the first part of his statement is true, I can but assume the same of the second.

"Well, what do you make of things?" I ask our intelligent friend.

"Ninety," he replies. "Fear means ninety in the lottery. I wanted to go and buy a ticket right after the first bombing, but I forgot. If I'd put a hundred lira on it then, I could have bought two hundred kilos of spaghetti and I would've been all set for the winter!"

"Go do it now," Figaro advises. "Third time's the charm."

"You mean they still have the lottery?" I ask.

"*Per forza!* Of course. You think the lottery would have collapsed just because Mussolini did? The only problem is that there's no number in the dream book for 'the final curtain.'"

"I think," I say, "that the Americans came to force Badolgio to the negotiating table. He's been in charge for forty-five days now, and the war drags on!"

"Maybe he's talking to them already," Figaro says.

"Yes, and maybe he's already signed the armistice," rejoins the clever little man. "Maybe Badolgio asked the Americans to come and dump a hundred tonnes of ordnance on us just so that the Germans wouldn't suspect that he's talking to the Allies."

"You think he'd have Rome bombed?"

"As if he cares about Rome! All he's interested in is the king and the princes. He'll make sure no bombs fall on them. When he's got our precious royal medal-collector in safety, he might spare a thought for the people."

"Which is precisely what they taught him at the Military Academy," Figaro says.

"Oh, but what else did they teach him? I may be small, but I'm clever, and I know how things stand. That midget isn't really even king. Have you ever seen a ten cent stamp with the old Umberto? Have you ever seen a picture of Queen Margherita? Never in the entire history of the house of Savoy has there been such a sour-faced little character as this Victor Emmanuel, our 'soldier-king'. What really happened was, Margherita had a daughter, and since there was not much prospect of a son to follow, they swapped it for the son of one of the washerwomen at court. That's the truth, I had it from my grandfather, who was a night watchman at the *Quirinale*. He even knew the washerwoman in question. He only told us on his deathbed. The king…"

"But he wasn't particularly a bad king…"

"He was a nothing sort of a king. His sole accomplishment was marrying the daughter of that Balkan goat-rustler, who ended up making quite a fine queen, even though she never really learned Italian."

"But he wasn't even a fascist!"

"Yes, and shall I tell you why? Because they couldn't agree who should have the first party membership card. After all, neither the king – Emperor of Abyssinia – nor the Duce could very well accept the number two card. So they left the old man out and only the princess of Piedmont joined the party. By the way, have you heard that if there's peace, Mussolini's daughter won't have to wear black underwear anymore?"

"What? Why?"

"Because they'll abolish the blackout in places of public entertainment. But that's not what I wanted to tell you. The king's job is to look after the constitution, yes? Well, about fifteen or sixteen years ago, a journalist asked the king to reinstate the constitution in an open letter, and unless Badolgio's let him out, he must still be in jail somewhere."

"Would you like a shave?" asks Figaro.

"Do you have hot water?"

"Yes."

"Then yes," I say "because hot water is a prime luxury."

"Do you know what happened in the spring? One of the former ministers requested an audience and told the king, 'Highness, things are not going well. But if you ever need someone, think of me!' What did the king do? Went and told Mussolini. He told on the minister, who of course was immediately arrested, and is still under police guard."

"I'm sure Badolgio's let him out," I say without much conviction.

"Maybe. But I doubt it occurred to him. Generals don't think."

"What about Eisenhower?" I ask from under the foam.

"He's a joke! An imbecile! A general!" the clever little man shouts, suddenly angry. "He's a raging fool! A professional officer. Don't you listen to the radio?"

"I listen to the BBC every day," I reply angrily.

"Well, then, you ought to know better."

"He won the battle for Sicily, and landed at Gela."

The clever little man breaks out in almost theatrical ironical laughter.

"Haha, 'won'. You know why? Because the other side was commanded by professional idiots too!" he says. Then he starts to explain. "One after the other. That's how they teach it at the Military Academy. If Eisenhower had been capable of thinking, he would have started with Sicily, Corsica and Sardinia. Last November there wasn't so much as a housecat there. But no, he was afraid, and after all, Morocco is closer to the States. He messed around there for months, and even got himself beaten a couple of times. If the British hadn't arrived from Benghazi, he'd still be sitting there now! Then Sicily. He should have taken Messina first, and sealed off the island. But no! He landed at Enna, cautiously, and the Germans ended up managing to clear all their armaments to the mainland. And, by the way, this wasn't on the BBC, but straight from a friend of mine in Catania, who told me that when the Americans landed, the first thing they brought on shore was an ice-cream machine!"

"Impossible!" Figaro says so indignantly he almost cuts me.

"It's the truth, I tell you. Luckily for them, that stretch of coastline was guarded by the local fascist militia, and they of course immediately surrendered at the sight of the mysterious machine. And then there's Gela! His crowning glory!"

"Did you want a close shave?" Figaro asks.

"You can't deny that they landed," I say stubbornly.

"Yes, that time they unpacked all their stuff and charged headlong inland. The only thing they forgot was their anti-tank guns. The Germans cottoned on at once, and the *panzers* came down from the hills. They would have driven them back into the sea in an hour. Lucky for us and democracy that the German general was even dumber than Eisenhower. He forgot that beyond the shore is the sea, and on the sea, the battleships of the American navy. When he got near the shore, thinking it was Dunkirk all over again, or the end of the world anyway, the cruisers spotted him. For the first time in history, battleships and tanks fought it out, and since battleships have bigger guns, the Nazis got creamed."

"They're already in Naples," I go on, "and in two weeks, they'll be here."

"Give them time. If there's some way of messing up, the Americans will find it."

"You don't really think it'll take them three months to get up here from Naples?"

"I'm short, but I'm clever," he replies. "Just wait and see!"

But my shave is finished, I'm hungry, and I'm in no mood to listen to pessimistic predictions.

"I'm off to the *Tor di Nona* to find some food," I say and leave. Because even if Victor Emmanuel is a bad king, he's the King, and king he will remain. Even if Eisenhower is a cowardly desk-jockey general, he's not going to stop being a general; but if I don't find something to eat, I'm going to go hungry. The only thing I've had today is Becker's tea, and by now I can feel I no longer care about anything, because the world begins and ends with me finding something to eat day after day. *Rimediare qualcosa* as they say in Italian, and rightly so, because literally this means to cure something, to find some relief for your what-ails-you, and hunger is indeed an ailment!

The *Tor di Nona* is barely two steps from here, just past the palace of the Papal Knight of the Rose. But the famous street is empty – the market has vanished.

Could it be the police, I wonder? But no. There are laws which neither bombs nor tyrants can alter. At critical times, goods disappear from the market. There's been a bombing. Tomorrow might bring peace, or an extended siege. The Americans might arrive with their plenty; or Badoglio and the Germans might fight it out, here, beneath the walls of the Capitol. Amidst this mess of historical possibility, the cornflour disappears without a trace.

I glance into the doorways in vain, I go into the little interior courtyards. In the aged, rickety sacristy of the abandoned church, I finally find the little old man selling contraband charcoal with the baroque putti looking on indulgently.

"Can I take two kilos?" I ask.

"Why not?" he says. And, as if he had figured out that I myself was lost in the search for the likeliest among the myriad possibilities, adds: "They might come back in a few hours and firebomb the entire city. And if the whole city is aflame, who on earth is going to want to buy charcoal?"

"The British know that the people here are good," I try to reassure him.

I have to go home empty-handed. I start off along the Tiber, towards the *Via Babuino*, Baboon Street. The 'blonde' Tiber – *flava Tiberis* – had its banks rebuilt in the last century according to the Parisian model, and all that's missing from under the plane trees are the little *bouquinistes*. Or rather, today there is something else missing too – the pedestrians. I am alone, hurrying along towards the Emperor Augustus' altar to peace, which – coincidentally – was inaugurated exactly three days before the outbreak of war. I'm trying not to think about lunch, and anyway, we still have a little food left. With considerable foresight, a long time ago, even before the battle of El Alamein, I had purchased something labelled *faricello*, and which I suspect could very well be the same thing that Persius in antiquity called *far scabiosum*, a rough oatmeal. They used to feed it to the chickens and other birds. Mixed in with it was a goodly amount of straw, and since the breaching of the Mareth-line, worms, too. In fact, as Diana carefully noted, little moth-like creatures have been flying up out of it since the fall of Tunis. Nonetheless, it's edible.

A little light-headed now, the charcoal under my arm, I'm beginning to think that it's not so bad. If the water's already on the boil, we can eat in twenty minutes – and it'll be quite a treat. It's a shame that the *faricello* is the cause of my only serious disagreements with Diana, since she stubbornly insists that she would rather starve to death than eat bird-food. Her moral standpoint, a hundred and eighty degrees from my own is not clearly explicable in psychological terms, but is rather because we came from totally different backgrounds. I had just been through a masterclass in homelessness and misery, while she was a student at the university. While I was busy learning which monasteries gave you a spoon for your soup, and to which you had to bring your own empty can, so they could slop the swill they called soup into it, she was busily experimenting with the more complicated recipes in

Pellaprat's *La cuisine familiale et pratique*. Thus, I am willing to cook the *faricello* as it is, and spit out the bits of straw, while she will spend a good deal of time, if there's nothing else for it, washing and cleaning it, before cooking it.

I've been trying to spin some legends around our main source of sustenance: I told her that Scottish rebels had fed on it, that Macbeth – even as king – had had it every day for breakfast, and that English racehorses became Derby winners on just such a diet. As for the worms, I assured her that Chinese gourmands were willing to pay vast sums for the pleasure of eating the oat-fed little creatures… at which point, she threatened to throw the whole lot (thirty kilos!) to the pigeons. Since when, it's only at times of revolution, bombardment and siege that I'm bold enough to suggest that we throw a handful into a pot.

It's noon, but the light is like gloaming. There's a big black cloud of smoke above the city, spreading over the parts still unaffected, over onto the Vatican hill. One of its pillars rests on the green pines of the Pincian hill. The wind blows unusual scents.

"If only I could take a few pig's ears to go with the *faricello*," I think to myself, "or if I had a spoonful of boiling oil and a little onion! Or a big dish of *faricello* with onions and sour cream and a big hunk of pork ribs… or strawberry jam and cheese, maybe with some coffee…" I swallow hard and break into a run with the charcoal, my heart beating fast as I climb the steps to the fifth floor of the house on the Street of Baboons, where – in the little glass cage, or let us say 'studio' – Diana is waiting for me.

To be completely accurate (since I'm writing memoirs and not a work of fiction) Diana is waiting for me in the little corridor between the staircase and the studio, blowing on the embers with an enormous fan. Her face is red, her hands are covered with soot as she waves to me:

"Tomorrow, there'll be peace."

"I couldn't find anything," I reply.

"That's ok, *mio caro*. I sold two nighties – you remember, I had two left, and bought beans and onions. We're ok for today."

I can see she was more afraid of the *faricello* than of the bombs.

I sit down at our little drawing-board table, on its four legs of two bricks each, and sigh: "Oh beans, oh peace!"

I first met Diana in the picture gallery in Brussels. She was still a virgin then, but was preparing with all her senses for her coming life as a woman. She was lovely, huge, and indescribably radiant. She was unconcerned that we stood in the grave silence marvelling at her nakedness, and fled – or tried to flee – only when a satyr's hairy hands reached for her naked flesh. The catalogue entry said only "Syrinx and Pan, by Jordaens, circa 1660. School of Rubens. Oil on canvas".

That was a long time ago, one peacetime weekday afternoon, and I could sit and stare at the painting.

I could see sparkling in Syrinx's strawberry blonde hair that light that Rubens picked up in Venice from Titian and Paris Bordone's pictures. This reddish colour was not mere painterly abstraction. It was in Venice that the German merchants met the Muslim spice-traders and the Balkan Slavs the heirs of the Lombards – the Queen of the Lagoon was back then partly Eastern slave-market, partly the gateway to the Mediterranean – and a never-before seen shade must have arisen in this cacophony of colours. Rubens merely superimposed this exotic shade onto the Flemish shoulders. The scene might well have come from Venice, for it was there that Aldus Manutius printed, under his dolphin-and-anchor imprint, the ancient legends in Greek – and so that everyone should understand them – in Latin, too; the adventures of Pan distilled into poetry. This is where Ovid's *Metamorphoses* were published, which tell us how Syrinx escaped Pan's unwanted advances by turning into reeds in his embrace. The landscape came to the Germanic studios in the sketchbooks of Heemskerk, Elsheimer, Dürer and countless other wanderers in Italy – the lights are northern, stormy, mysterious. Europe spent centuries drawing, painting, and mixing colours so that out of them should emerge this legendary nymph who cheated Pan in the rushes.

When we met again, in Rome, Syrinx sat with her hair pinned up, in a skirt and blouse, and told me that her real name was Diana. I recognised her immediately, but I couldn't bring myself to tell her that I knew all about her little adventure with Pan, and so I merely introduced myself with a polite smile. Not long after that, she came up to my little glass house on the roof in the Street of Baboons, and stayed.

Some future, law-abiding reader may ask whether the fact that she stayed meant that I married her. I did not. Social conventions are the first victims of war. Borders dissolve, people die even though they're healthy, and the most ingrained prejudgements disappear in the daily mass of final judgements. Diana, in a fit of enthusiasm, once even asked after the price of a gold wedding band, and went to see a lawyer friend of hers to find out what kind of papers we'd need to get married. As far as her papers were concerned, she was pleased to find that she did not need the consent of her parents, (had she needed it she would never have got it), since she was three months past her twenty-first birthday. My situation was different, though. I would have needed documents from the Consulate, the Foreign Ministry and the Ministry of the Interior, all sorts of things from the Hungarian military, leave to remain, proof of address, tax number… Diana studied the twenty-four item long list of documents I didn't have and couldn't get, melancholically, and finally established that the only one I could get my hands on was my vaccination book.

Since she knew Italian literature and was therefore aware from reading Manzoni's *The Betrothed,* that waiting for the blessing of officialdom in such matters could take a very long time indeed, she put off these administrative hurdles until the return of peace, forever around the corner.

I could say, then, that we shared a bed and a table. But since I have undertaken to tell the truth in these memoirs and nothing but the truth, I cannot in all sincerity say this either. For we didn't have a table – it took me some time to find that drawing-board which now stood on its foundation of bricks, waiting for my soup, and our bed was a mattress on the stone floor. In the strict sense of the term, all we really shared was a broom-handle, which rested on two nails in a corner and served in place of a wardrobe. On its right side hung my suit for important occasions, which is to say my less-crumpled one, and on the left paraded Diana's clothes which, despite the hurry, she had nonetheless managed to pack, and the two nighties that had now become our lunch. Although it's also true that in summer we sweltered together in the little glass house which became a veritable glass-house, and in winter shivered together under the entire stock of clothes in our stick-wardrobe – for this we did not need the written permission of the Minister of the Interior. You could justly call this way of life poverty, but we did not experience it as such.

We had a piano. It was only a rented piano, of course, which were easy to come by because the eighty-eight keys spoke the music of the well-fed. People returned their rented instruments, and bought a bag of potatoes instead. An extra meal or two wouldn't have made much difference to us by that point anyway, and so we decided to place between ourselves and total squalor good old powder-wigged Johann Sebastian Bach.

"If we have a son, his name will be Johann Sebastian," Diana said.

We didn't find the poverty oppressive, because everything is relative, but suffering is especially so. Diana had a good quote from Italian literature for this, too: Dante's *Inferno* had many circles and crannies. In the hell of 1943, on whose gates you really could never have inscribed that it was made by primordial love and ultimate intellect; and about which you could not say that justice drove its maker (with his little Chaplin-moustache), many many such little evil crannies bled one into another down, down, into the ones where little children suffocated in the poison gas… in this hell, then, the *bolgia della miseria* belonged to the higher circles; an enviable state even, whose fire you could look on as cleansing flames.

At least we weren't sat on the outskirts of town in the depths of some miserable rented courtyard. Rather we presided over the street of artists and antiquaries from the dignified heights of our rooftop perch. Here, poverty went about in fancy dress, and was known locally as *'la bohéme'*. This is the urban equivalent of the rural form of the concept, which is usually referred to as an 'idyll'. We looked out over

177

other, distant, glass houses, where pictures and sculptures were born; we knew the painters, who could walk around in clothes spotted and stained with acrylic, the sculptors with their hands covered in clay – the true bohemians who had no use for barbers, because everybody knew they were poets or actors. From here, you could see all the way to St Cecilia's Academy of Music, where the cellos stood in neat rows and where those who knew their way around backstage could sneak in for the occasional dress rehearsal. Of the many faces of Rome, it was the Rome of the *via Margutta* and the *via Babuino* where poverty was not oppressive, nor an object of shame. There you could happily walk around in trousers through whose worn mesh-like fabric your bare knees protruded, as if you had been merely disinclined to make a choice among the many others in your wardrobe. This was a good thing.

"I've never in my life been to a single museum," Mussolini once admitted in a candid moment, taking a quick break from expounding the superiority of Italian culture. He was undoubtedly telling the truth – a picture gallery is no place for a dictator to make an impression. He was happy to have his picture taken as a miner or pilot, on horseback or in a hard-hat, in a lion's cage petting his favourite pet, but even he somehow understood that he would make a poor impression among the *condottieri* hanging around the museums. He made up for it by going to exhibitions. Since the vast majority of the state's income was distributed among state employees or fascist party members by way of wages (or more simply misappropriated), the rest went towards convincing the people of the fantastic accomplishments attained on its behalf. This is what the world's first state-sponsored Ministry of Propaganda was for – an organ of self-aggrandisement – as well as the enormous *mostra*s, that odd mixture of museum, exhibition and fair; this is what kept the painters and sculptors of the *via Margutta* and the *via Babuino* in business.

It was in these two parallel hillside niches (which in antiquity had housed Sallust's gardens) that freedom, preserved from tyranny by force of necessity, found a home. Court jesters must once have had similar rights of freedom of speech. Papal authority, although limitless, preserved the *jus murmurandi*, and if you held your tongue under the black-shirts they would leave you be. The brownshirts went further and required you to bay with the wolfpack. But you can neither produce nor replace artists, and so you have to be careful with them; its best simply to close your ears if they wish something on someone with their hands and eyes turned to heaven. Without artists, there are neither paintings nor sculptures, and without paintings and sculptures, there's no eternal glory. Il Duce was happiest when he could see himself on the sort of fresco like the one on the wall of the state room of the unfinished stadium, near the (also) unfinished Ministry of Foreign Affairs. In this fresco he was painted in a steel helmet and black shirt, mounted on a coal-black steed, riding at the head of the Cianos, Grandis and Balbos (who were all on smaller horses). An allegory of Victory hovering behind his head, a picture of Italy behind city walls, raising its hands in fascist salute, at his feet. In one of the lower corners, muscle-bound men built a tower out of metal cogs, while in another a group of women reaped, and in yet another weaned their infants. From the background, blackshirted youths with triangular flags and Roman standards rushed with bayonetted soldiers to the scene of the action. The corners as yet unfilled are populated by flocks of drawn-in eagles. His favourite sculptor was the one whose theme was "the idea of Empire is born from the Duce's mind", and showed him with powerful jaw and bald pate, a sort of rising platform sunk in the top of his head, from which Pallas Athena emerges, sword and shield in hand. "Jupiter and Minerva" the more educated (which is to say the ones who had finished high school) journalists whispered to one another, and the Ministry of Propaganda's order of the day was that eight column inches, headed in bold, were to be dedicated to the statue.

The two streets of artists were kept busy even during the war. While the Germans were enjoying their Polish honeymoon, Mussolini was still waiting to see how things would turn out, and – because he could hardly say any of this in public and dictators always have to have something to say to the public – went on organising the 1942 World's Fair. And while the

179

shivering Calabrian footsoldiers were freezing their toes off in the Albanian highlands, the *via Margutta* was busily working on the female figures for the exhibition's Palace of Peace and Civilisation. The Fair was officially postponed after Wavell's conquest of Benghazi, but there wasn't a single fascist minister who dared pull the plug on the project as a whole. "We'll hold it after the final victory", they said. And when the last starving colonial soldier surrendered to the British, so that they could finally have a crust of bread and a cup of tea, on that day of total defeat, the time had come to commission a statue of the Victory of Revenge to be erected on the appropriate spot, come the day of final victory. The police opened a competition for a memorial to the *carabinieri* fallen in Abyssinia. Its inscription was ready-made, but the figures decorating the base of the obelisk went to Africa straight from the *via Margutta.*

Hitler went all the way to Sweden for the granite blocks for the memorial to the fall of France, but the cautious Italians made do for the moment with plaster. They covered the plaster statues with water and clay, so that on photographs they would look like they were carved out of natural stone. The main thing was that the artists had work, and with the money from the reliefs of epic battles they could buy charcoal and spaghetti. Those lucky enough to be commissioned to do a Saint Sebastian or a Saint Theresa for some Vatican monsignore in between two "tank battles of the Giants and Titans", could even afford real coffee, which brought a smile to the lips of their thirsty models.

Of the tragic face of fascism, which began with its cudgels and castor oil, and culminated in the German firing squads and deportations, the *via Margutta* saw little, being more exposed to the grotesque. The dictator is not a terror to whoever can spit his plaster likeness straight in the eye the moment they take it out of the mould. Perhaps that's why the mediaeval illuminators liked to paint grotesque little devils in their books – so that they should not be frightened of the real thing. If Mussolini, in his twenty years in power could have overheard, for a bare twenty minutes the speculations of the artisans glazing his plaster casts bronze, about the identity and various body-parts of his late mother, he would have banned people from making statues of him outright.

But he never did overhear, and the artists lived off the statues of the Duce ordered by every school, nursery, railway station, office, shop and barbershop in the country. He didn't know that there were only two institutions left in Italy where the average citizen could go without seeing his protruding eyes and more and more pronounced jaw, and where they could finally breathe easy at the absence of the sight: the churches and the brothels. He didn't know that there's an old tradition of buying busts – the ancient Romans used their obscene statues of Priapus to frighten off harmful birds. Later, they used ox's horns painted red to stop themselves from getting poked in the eye, and now they looked to the prominent jaw of the Duce to protect them from the greatest danger of all: the police. The average citizen could expect to meet the police at any hour of the day and especially night, because he had "said something", or had been thinking aloud. And what better defence if the police did turn up with the bully boys of the local militia than to point to the top of the piano where, in between Verdi and Beethoven (but far larger, of course) sat the Duce, and to say, "but gentlemen, look, here he is in pride of place, the MAN, whom his Holiness Pius IX called the Man sent by Providence, the drainer of marshes, he who made order on the railways. How could you, for even a moment, doubt that I believe, fight and obey?!"

We observed the streets of artists from our little glass perch on the roof. It was from here that we were witness, six weeks ago, to the twilight of the statues. It was night, a quiet, very dark night in July. Suddenly, the silence was broken, and a faint but growing buzz penetrated the night, like on new year's eve when the bells of all the churches strike midnight. All the windows in the neighbourhood were at once thrown open and there was the cacophony of rejoicing. There were few people who still listened to the local radio – most Romans looked to the BBC to tell them what was going on in their homeland – but those few woke the district in the space of just a few minutes, rousing the neighbours, and shouting across the alleys. In a few minutes, the avalanche of noise

181

grew, and the loudspeakers were now repeating from the opened windows: "This afternoon, by order of his Highness the King, *Cavaliere* Mussolini was relieved of his position as leader of the country's government and placed under arrest. Marshal Badoglio has taken over at the head of government. Italy fights on". Everyone ignored that last sentence. The main thing was that Mussolini, master of life and death, had become nothing more than a simple *cavaliere*, a knight. He was a mere mortal, and what's more, he was under arrest. His busts flew heavily out of the open windows, his portraits arced, floated, and finally fell to ground. That was the night when Diana and I were truly sorry, for the first time in our lives, that we didn't own a bust of Mussolini.

The historian may be surprised that this news was not followed immediately by a bloodbath. That the masses, now free, did not take up their kitchen knives and go in search of the terrified fascists who had – until bedtime that evening – still been in power. The explanation is simple – everyone had a portrait of the Duce, and everyone could throw it out of the window. The next day, it was not in a sea of blood and broken bodies that the passer-by on the street was mired up to the ankle, but rather in plaster and broken glass.

I saw what was perhaps the last intact statue of Mussolini left in the city the next day in the *piazza San Silvestro*. It was wearing unusual headgear, and someone told me the story.

It seems an old man had taken it there in a wheelbarrow. The statue was covered by canvas, and its unveiling was not easy. The old man was elegantly dressed in a black suit and – unusually for July – was even wearing a black waistcoat, a thick, old-fashioned gold watch-chain across its front. He was solemn as a loving uncle at his niece's wedding. He pulled down his trousers and proceeded to give the Duce a covering for his bald head. Then he neatly tidied up his person and his clothes and took a bow before the hurriedly assembled crowd.

"Gentlemen, I beg your forgiveness! Pardon me, *vi prego*. I had made an oath, *un voto*."

The applause that greeted him and the statue was more sincere than any the Duce had ever heard in real life. When

I got there, there was an admiring throng around the statue, and I overheard the following:

"What starts with castor oil, ends in shit," and this sounded very much like the final word of the chorus in a Greek tragedy.

Now, in the expectation of imminent peace, the festive atmosphere of that night came back to us. "I wonder what Eckstein has to say about this," Diana said.

"He'll probably come up and tell us in a bit," I replied.

Eckstein is my friend, we have many things in common. We both learned the basics of Roman history in the Theresianum in Vienna, and we both try and solve the same ninety-one problems each month: paying rent and having something to eat thirty times in the morning, and another thirty each at noon, and in the evening. It's a little easier for him since he's a bachelor, and sometimes gets invited for lunch or dinner here or there; indeed, he likes to come and see us between one and two, which reduces the number of his problems by one, and increases mine by the same number. But I am glad to have Eckstein as my 'parasite' (in the ancient sense of the word, as guest at table), as someone to converse with, that friend whose unbroken optimism is most welcome precisely at mealtimes. Was Eckstein so wise as to be able to predict how things would turn out? Or had the Lord blessed him with a special sort of colour-blindness – an inability to see what was black? Perhaps he, too, like so many others, was merely too meek to admit that Hitler would storm even the last strongholds of culture, and that Mussolini could ride his iron mount all the way to Alexandria. I'm not a novelist, and don't know what lies in people's hearts – I can describe only their faces, record nothing more than their words.

Eckstein looked uncannily like Don Quixote and with his flat, yellow teeth, also a little like Rocinante; only the pointed beard was missing to complete the resemblance back then, an omission he soon corrected. He lived in Rome with his pre-war Austrian papers and somehow managed to disappear from the records of the various ministries when, following the Anschluss, he made an executive decision to ignore the orders and didn't show up at the German embassy to register himself. The Italians, in any event, had a guilty conscience when it came to the Austrians. After the Dollfuss murder, Mussolini emerged onto his balcony and, hand on hip, declared: "*Chi tocca l'Austria, tocca noi! – Whoever harms Austria, harms us!*" Away from the balcony, and after the Anschluss, he remarked about this episode, "no-one had asked us to do it, and no-one thanked us for it, either". And if the Italian authorities cut the Austrians some slack, there was another reason, too: Austria had been, in the last hundred years from Napoleon to Franz Josef, the only 'enemy'. And a good old enemy is still closer to our hearts than a bad new friend.

It was nice to meet Eckstein at the various low points of the war. One afternoon in September, Dietrich, the head of the German press office called a press conference and announced: "Gentlemen, the German offensive is over. In two or three days, we will capture Moscow. There is no longer anything resembling co-ordinated resistance. Our task now is merely to liquidate the scattered Soviet troops still remaining in Russia."

Our official comforter in times of need, the BBC, could only counter with a single sunk submarine, and our dreams that night were disturbed and uneasy. The panzer divisions would turn away now from the East, force France into the Axis, which Franco would then join... with their French and Spanish allies, the Axis would take Gibraltar, and under the protection of Krupp's guns, would march into Africa. Their chain of submarine ports would stretch from Dakar to Narvik. The Italians would occupy Egypt, the victorious Nazis would stroll into the Caucasus and force Turkey into the war with an ultimatum – and then push forward to meet the Italians, via Baghdad, on the banks of the Nile. Under the protection of the combined German, Italian and French fleets, the Wehrmacht would cross the channel and Sir Oswald Mosley would become the new Prime Minister of England, because he's the only one Hitler will talk to...

This is the nightmare scenario I take to Eckstein.

"Did you hear what Dietrich said?"

"I have more reliable sources of information," Eckstein replies with boundless calm, and points to the book he's just been reading – *War and Peace*.

"But Dietrich said…"

"Napoleon's mistake," he continues unabashed, "was failing to take into account the Russian winter. Tolstoy describes how there was a metre of snow around Smolensk in October already. And by Christmas…"

"But that was a hundred and thirty years ago!"

Eckstein looks at me like the Sad Faced Knight at Sancho Panza when he doesn't know who Amadis de Gaula was.

"The climate of Smolensk has not changed in that time."

"But the war…"

"And neither has war. In a metre of snow, there is no Luftwaffe, because the airstrips simply disappear. There's nothing to bomb either, because everything is covered in a blanket of snow. There are no tanks, because every one of them would need a snowplough to go ahead of it. There's no re-supply by truck, because the engine coolant freezes. And feet in 1941 will freeze off just the same as they did in 1812."

"But he said the war was over!"

"Yes, and Napoleon said the same thing, with the difference that he said it at the gates of the Kremlin. Tolstoy describes vividly how the Russians fought in the snow, since they knew full well that it would indeed snow. They came out of the forests, surprised the retreating French, set fire to their stores. *Pazienza* – patience. Let's wait and see – in two weeks it'll be October, and our reliable ally, General Winter, will arrive."

Three short and one long knocks signal that Eckstein has divined Diana's wish, and is now outside our door with a brand new optimistic take on events.

"Well?" I say as I let him in.

I can see my friend's delight when he notices that instead of *faricello*, there's leftover beans at the bottom of the pot, and that Diana has already started to wash up the dish (that I had anyway licked clean) in his honour.

"*Andiamo bene.* All is well, peace is coming," he says.

"Oh beans! Oh peace!" I say again.

"I have it on excellent authority that an American General was already here last night. He came by plane, landed on the *Ciampioni*, and talked over everything. Tomorrow, the British paratroopers will come and take the city."

185

"How do you know?"

"This morning, a certain colonel came to see Ariane, and afterwards Ariane and I had lunch."

"Would you like some beans, nonetheless?" Diana asks, more out of politeness, since she is perfectly aware that these lunches tend not to spoil Eckstein's appetite, and then adds: "Ariane's information is usually reliable."

"Ariane is indeed a good and reliable creature," Eckstein accedes, "and now that we're reading *Iphigenia,* and she's starting to penetrate Goethe's spiritual universe, with my guidance of course, I'm really pleasantly surprised by her extraordinary spiritual sensibility."

"Yes, and she's not bad looking, either," I say. "No wonder she's got as high as colonel."

"What exactly did Ariane say?" Diana interrupts quickly.

"That's all, but that's enough. The situation is so obvious that even a child could deduce the next steps. It's the endgame now. Mate in three moves."

"*Ecco!* Here are your beans," Diana announces.

For the next two minutes, Eckstein becomes supremely ignorant of the existence of colonels and generals, Iphigenia and Ariane vanish from his mental horizon. Only after he's carefully wiped the plate clean with his index finger, and then licked it dry with his tongue, does he return to earthly things.

"The situation is as follows. At this very moment the British are in the process of, or have already finished, occupying Taranto. Since Augusta and the other Sicilian bases are already in Allied hands, the Mediterranean routes are open, and the British and the Americans can come and go as they please. Full stop. The Americans will take Naples, and with that, the question of the munitions the Germans managed to get over onto the mainland is also settled."

"Full stop," I say approvingly.

"Furthermore, the paratroopers will come, occupy the buildings of the more significant institutions, the radio and the railway stations, or rather," and he points at the slowly shifting, but nonetheless still grey cloud of smoke, "what remains of them, so that Badolgio, saving face, can go to the

186

Germans and tell them that he has surrendered to over-whelming force. He is then free to go over to the Allies."

"Who? Him and his dog?" Diana asks.

"Not quite," Eckstein replies unruffled, and draws a circle in the air with his finger, "with the whole country. The British only want the Italian army because at the moment it's an enemy. But the Italian railwaymen can mess up the three northerly rail routes overnight. The *carabinieri*, who are stuck in the nineteenth century, can blow up a couple of dozen key bridges. Suddenly the German armies in Italy are captive. Full stop. The Germans can bomb a city or two in their misery, but that's nothing really serious. They don't have the capacity in any case, for carpet bombing any more."

"No, the only German carpet that's playing an active part in the war is the one being chewed by Hitler," I say.

"I can just see," Eckstein says (and it is with this same expression that he now adopts that he must have explained to Ariane why Iphigenia yearned for the Greek homeland), that the advanced forces of the Fifth and Eighth Armies, with air support, will breach the system of defences Brenner built over twenty years in a matter of days. And that's not the Maginot line that you could simply go around. These are the Alps and the Dolomites, that can defend Italy from possible Nazi revenge attacks. From the plains of the *Po*, the Liberators are then free to level the factories of Linz and the aircraft plants in Wiener Neustadt. *Wir werden ihre Städte ausradieren!* Hitler screamed. Well, something very similar is going to happen to them. But maybe it won't be necessary at all if the two or three hundred thousand Italians stationed in Greece turn on the Germans there. Those are weak troops, because anyone worth their salt is fighting in Russia now, where – by the way – the Nazis have just organised their first ever retreat in summer."

"All according to plan," I nod.

"And then the British can land wherever they want in the Balkans, and even if they only come with one man and his dog, it'll be fine as long as they bring guns. And I'm not even talking about the latest technology – the guns they captured off the Italians and Germans in Africa will do. The Greek and Yugoslav partisans, given guns, grenades and mortars, will sweep the

Balkans clear of the Germans in days. Then they'll start in on each other a bit too, *pazienza,* but they will nonetheless still drive the Germans out. In the meanwhile, a strong British contingent can break through towards the Drava, join up with the partisans, and head for Ploesti. Ploesti and the oilfields are the goal, that's where the Italians and the Greeks will attack, and the Bulgarians will join them, driving out their Quisling, whatever the hell his name is. The Romanians won't be naïve enough to sacrifice whatever troops they still have left after Stalingrad, and will open their gates before the advancing Soviets."

"Full stop?"

"Colon. Or rather, semi-colon. In two weeks, the Southern front will no longer be an issue. The situation is similar to the one in 1918 when the British broke into Syria and Palestine. Turkey and Bulgaria surrendered and the *Entente* troops came up from the South while Hindenburg and his lot were still dreaming of *Siegfridstellung*s. Only this time, there won't be time for dreaming."

"And it'll all be over by the end of the year?"

"*Per forza.* For sure. You don't seriously think the Germans could possibly last another winter? In October the British and Soviets will meet in the Balkans, and then the Balkan army – and quite a mixed army it will be – will move up through Hungary, and then the Hungarians will join, of course…"

"I hope so," I say. "Although the example of 1918 goes to show that we Hungarians are prone to fighting for lost causes; for hopeless causes even – against the Tatars, the Turks… I wouldn't be surprised if…"

"Forget your unhappy paradoxes! We're talking about the final act, the last few weeks of the war. In November, while the Soviets attack along the entire Eastern front, and Germany is paralysed by lack of Romanian oil, the Allies will land in Southern France and start working up to Paris. The Germans will get a taste of their own medicine – since the Atlantic wall is impregnable, they'll simply go around it. They might even land in Denmark, in which case the Swedes would demand that Germany leave Norway – should Hitler refuse, they would invade. This time, the landings in Trondheim and Narvik would succeed, and the shipments of iron ore would stop. In December, co-ordinated bombing from British and Italian airfields will start, and by the first of January, there'll be peace. Peace, full stop."

"Excellent. But what if Badoglio doesn't go over? After all, he's been dictator now for forty-five days, and so far his constant refrain has been that he'll continue to fight alongside the Axis!"

"Forty-five days – it just goes to prove what I told you. You can't simply turn around in this day and age and say, 'oh sorry, turns out the Western plutocracies are not so bad after all, and all that about German-Italian unity was just so much chin music.' It would only confuse the Allies if the Italians stopped their organised retreat and started an organised advance overnight instead. The time of military improvisation has passed. Seriously – these forty-five days prove that Badoglio is working everything out to the smallest detail. He's giving the British time to transfer their African airbases over to Northern Italy. He's giving the Soviets information as to where they should start their winter offensive. In other words, he needed these forty-five days, full stop."

"When is it that the paratroopers are coming, today or tomorrow?" Diana asks.

"The colonel was not precise."

"I can understand that," I say. "I know Ariane, and if I were in her shoes..."

"Yes, we'll, I'll make sure you never find yourself in her shoes!" interrupted Diana kindly but firmly. "Anyway, I'm convinced that our friend is right, but don't forget that if her calculations are correct, there are still seventy days when we need to find ourselves lunch and dinner!"

"There's the *faricello*..." I risk, because I can see how good a mood Eckstein's predictions have put her in, "thirty kilos over seventy days, that works out at..."

"Why don't you go and try and get us some supper?" she replies, as if I hadn't just brought up the topic of our most valuable possession...

"Couldn't we have another cup of tea?" I ask. "Since peace is just around the corner, it doesn't make sense to hoard it any more."

"The fire's gone out."

"Yes, and I have to go too," Eckstein remarks. "Come, let's go have an ersatz coffee somewhere."

We go out. Having a coffee has become a ceremonial event which entails leaning on the marble surface of the café's table, waiting for a cup of something bitter and black. This infernal brew is made from the Sicilian *trigonella* plant, and the only thing that makes it sweeter is the knowledge that Sicily is now once more under the wing of democracy. The barman, if you're not faint of heart, will dash something alcoholic that tastes of aniseed and saccharine into it too. Refreshed by this bastard concoction, Eckstein returns to predicting the near future.

"When I said January, I was really taking a very pessimistic view of events. It'll only be that late if the Prussian High Command will put up with their Austrian Chancellor's shenanigans even after the collapse of the Italian and Balkan fronts. The most likely eventuality is what happened here: he'll be arrested and replaced with some general. It doesn't matter who, of course, he only has to have the right number of buttons on his uniform. The general won't wait to be mated, since he knows the rules of the game, and will concede. No, it won't be seventy days at all!"

"*Speriamo bene,*" I say, and on this optimistic note we part, the same as everyone else these days.

En route to my patient I take a shortcut through the heart of old Rome, and I notice that the bronze doors of the Pantheon are open. Did someone open it? Or did someone leave it open? It's a good feeling to step, for a moment, into eternal peace, and look up through the round central eye of the ceiling at the cloudy afternoon sky. The augurs would have been waiting to see whether an eagle or two would fly past, and if they did, whether they were flying from the left or the right. I am looking at the sky to see if our saviours the paratroopers won't come falling out of it, just as the baroque putti in the frescoes on the ceiling of the church of *San Ignazio* float out of the clouds to join hands in lifting the saint up to heaven... but there isn't even a cloud big enough to hide them.

The *Largo Argentina* is not far from here, with its huge old apartment buildings overlooking the columns and round altars of the old forum in the middle of the square and its mediaeval tower made of Roman stone, where instead of sentries with pikes, bus conductors now mill around. In one of these buildings lives Bananawoman.

I didn't always know my patients' real names. Sometimes, all I remember of them is their illnesses, a few words, or perhaps an odour. I called her that because she used to sell bananas with her daughter in the *Campo de'Fiori* market before the war. The bananas and the Empire are both long gone, but the state monopoly on bananas lives on. In fact, the employees of the State Banana Monopoly continued to draw their pay, and go to work promptly at nine every day, in order that they should – in the fifth year of the country being utterly devoid of bananas – continue to telephone the Colonial Ministry and try to settle their still-outstanding affairs. The market banana-sellers, though, did get temporary permits to sell other things too. When I started treating her neuralgia, Bananawoman was selling mostly cabbages, sometimes potatoes and occasionally fish. In any event, she dealt in edibles and therefore her chronic nervous pains were one of the important weapons in my fight against starvation. The hawkers and vendors of the *Campo de'Fiori* were a select lot, and were mostly linked by ties of blood. Bananawoman herself had a cousin who sold ox lung, innards, and tripe, the profession of *tripparolo* being a separate one in Rome from the butchers. By late afternoon, there's nothing left in the market, and the bronze statue of Giordano Bruno looks on resignedly from his bird's-eye view as the market litter is swept away. But there's all sorts of things to be had in the little alternative markets inside people's flats. You could even get pig's feet from time to time (ox-legs having been requisitioned by the Naval Ministry, who maintained that they were using them to make grease for submarines), or funny little bits of meat which went under the collective name of "shredded rabbit". To what extent the appearance on the market of these tasty morsels was related to the disappearance of the cats that otherwise traditionally roamed the area between the Forum and the Pantheon is not for me to say, and

I will leave it for the future miners of posterity. There were times when people were selling lamb's throats, because it turned out you could make soup out of them. Good, caring Mother Nature had hidden some fat in between the gristle, and so in my increasingly frequent moments of hopelessness, I came and took advantage of my patient's gratitude to *rimediare qualcosa*, or get something to eat.

The uninitiated will surely wonder, looking at the houses around the *Largo Argentina* (which has about as much to do with Argentina as Leicester Square does with Leicester. Actually, that's not quite true, the legend being that when Attila the Hun conquered the city of Argentina, and had its walls demolished, he personally changed its name to Strassburg, and so it's Strassburg's former name that the *Largo Argentina* preserves) that a market stallholder should live in an apartment in one of these palatial buildings. But the moment you step inside the apartment, you'll understand – and it's part of a doctor's profession to analyse their patients' speech, their environment.

When Mussolini... now that I'm once more writing his name, it makes me realise that I've done it so many times today that a reader of some distant future may come to the conclusion that he was an important man. Not so – but the man with a toothache will talk only about his tooth, and a cardiac patient will forever be feeling for his pulse. Where Italy's problems were concerned, the name of the pathogen causing them inevitably came up. Anyhow, when Mussolini went and had a go at the ancient Rome and did more damage than any fleet of enemy bombers, new districts emerged on the outskirts of the city. The inhabitant of the age-old streets, now homeless, could have moved to these new quarters, but didn't. There were those whose profession tied them to their old quarter, but many were simply afraid of the soulless new apartment-blocks. "I'll live on bread and onions if I have to – but I'll stay in Rome" the devotees of the city thought, and didn't emigrate; "Better a bed in the *Urbs* than a flat in the alien new *Via Appia*, or on the *Monte Sacra*... in the back of beyond". And so, in the tradition of the catacombs, a new and secret city came into being in the old apartments. The big rooms were divided into three or four parts, corridors and passageways appeared in the larger spaces; sometimes, they even pierced the party wall between two houses and added half a room to a quarter of a larder to make a living space. The beds nested one on top of the other, while in the taller rooms galleries were built, on which a cobbler's workshop would operate, or a sewing machine would clatter busily away. Sometimes you had to climb a ladder to see a bedridden patient, while the people underneath you below the gallery would be doing their ironing, or having their supper, or reading. In the evenings, they would separate the close family from the guests with improvised paper or textile Chinese screens. People cooked on little charcoal stoves in these rooms, preferably by the window so the smoke and carbon dioxide could escape (or they made a makeshift chimney by punching a hole in the wall). There were communal kitchens and bathrooms, too, secret chambers and, as befitting life in an old *palazzo*, hidden doors in the wall. Bananawoman and her family lived in just such an apartment.

"What do you make of this terrible bombing?" she asks.

"Was it so terrible?" I reply.

"Indeed. My brother-in-law was there, he saw the whole thing. Some of the bombs hit the cemetery, and unearthed the dead, while the rest fell on the little streets around *San Lorenzo* station and buried the living."

I can feel that she's right. All I could think about this morning was the strategic position, history, and the future (and of course, lunch), but I forgot that the bombing has victims. I think for a moment – no, I don't know anyone around there, or do I? On All Souls, not having any dead of my own in the city's ground (and therefore not having roots here myself), I went out to the Verano cemetery, where permanent immigrants to Rome are buried. On a flat, white grave was written:

> Gud som haver barnen kär
> Ser til mig som liten är

A bedtime prayer for Swedish children – "My Lord, who has but love for children, look down upon me, and see my littleness". I imagine this little boy, kneeling in his long white nightgown, as if praying in a drawing by Willibeek Le Maire, and suddenly shudder – what if he's been hurt?

"You're right, it's terrible – sad," I reply, this time very sincerely.

"Do you think there'll be bombings every day?" she asks, perhaps because she's gotten used to my mental bag of reassuring phrases.

I can't talk to her about Ariane's colonel, so I simply say, "I think Badoglio will soon make peace."

"*Magari*! That the Good Lord make it so! Things haven't changed much since he took over."

"Ah, but fascism is finished…"

"We're still exactly where we were before. Previously, it was the police and the fascist militia guarding the market. Every one of them stole, they all demanded bribes. If you brought a basket of eggs to market, you had to give two dozen away as a 'present'. The militia's gone now, but the police are demanding twice as much as they did before."

"What do they do with all that food? Surely they can't eat all that!"

"Don't you know? They offload it in the *Tor di Nona* and the black-marketeers sell it for them!"

"But the police raid the *Tor di Nona* too! The little boys stand lookout on the *Ponte Sant'Angelo* and if they see them coming, they shout '*piove*' [it's raining]. The square is empty before the police make it past the corner!"

"Yes, everybody knows that. The police know too. They come and pretend they have nothing to do with the business there. But sometimes, a rival patrol will come, who work with the market in *Porta Portensé*, and then they confiscate everything and sell it over there. There's practically no-one left who comes to the *Campo de'Fiori*, because we're legal and so have almost nothing other than cabbages to sell."

I can see that now is the time for me to come to the point. "You wouldn't happen to have a little *polenta*?"

"Not a grain, of course. But I can let *you* have half a kilo."

"Those poor people over in *San Lorenzo*," I sigh again.

"Oh, and before I forget, cousin Paula asked me to send you over there the next time I saw you."

"I'll go see her now," I say, "and thanks again!"

In my medical practice, I am used to people forwarding me hither and thither. I am a ball in my patients' hands, and they represent my fate. I share their pain for a while, I worry for them, a unity of fate, and then they send me on to someone who likewise has neuralgia or varicose veins. I go from environment to environment, and sometimes I feel like an actor who has to learn new roles again and again, to recite different words. Here, someone wants me to tell them serious things with a knowledgeable frown, that I should be their doctor and no-one else's, while there, they want to chat with me in Norwegian. The great Galen boasts that he treated the Emperor just the same as the slave – but could he converse the same with both? Didn't he have to adapt his words, his references, his gestures just as much as his treatments?

Bananawoman now sends me flying from the ancient Rome to the personal little Paris of Madame Pauline, who's French; Bananawoman is the only one to call her *sora Paola*.

Madame Pauline lives at the other end of the little street that's come into being in the enormous apartment – I know the way already. Straight ahead in the darkness to the little candle ahead, then left, and – with a loud '*permesso?*' through the room which serves as a sewing-shop during the day; then left again, and into the dead-end where her door lies. I know the rules, too, I have to knock four times softly and loudly twice.

'"Your life is a novel," Sándor Török said, "you just have to write it". And how could this life fail to be a novel, the life of a Frenchwoman who lives here, now, behind a door that opens only to those who know the secret code? But since the narrative of every novel can be quickly summarised, I will tell you that she was a young woman when her passionately amorous husband brought her to Rome. She had a boy, then two girls – perfect twins. And then her husband left. From there to life behind her closed door was but a shortish step.

Alfonso, her son, opens the door.

"*Bon jour, docteur.* My mother is out. Would you be so kind as to wait for her?"

"If she won't be terribly long."

Alfonso strokes his beard – the kind one only sees nowadays on submariners – and says: "I'm working on the new locomotive. It's smaller than the old one, but I'm going to rebuild that one. I'm going to cast the wheels. Look, I'm making the moulds already. I'll melt the lead on the charcoal stove. I'm making some progress, at last."

"Of course," I say. "Although I liked the last one too."

"It's terribly simplistic. Have you seen the new rails?" he asks, and points to the ceiling. "The first ones are hanging up there."

"Very interesting. Is the armoured wagon ready yet?"

"Yes, but I'll have to rebuild that, too."

I sit down on the bed while Alfonso returns to his clay mould. He's working. He is the first person I've met today who isn't talking about the bombing, or politics.

"The poor idiot," my reader must be thinking. But not at all – extraordinary times make extraordinary men – *c'est tout.* Alfonso is quite sane, in fact he's a very talented linguist, with whom I like talking, because he corrects me when I mix Italian words into my French.

When the war came, and Mussolini was waiting to see which way the wind would blow, Alfonso was an apprentice baker, and the twins had just started working in a hairdresser's. They were barely getting by. That was just around the time when the German scouts came looking for guest workers – they promised them a hundred lira a day instead of the twenty they were getting at home, and three-month contracts, so Alfonso went. He struggled with the frenetic pace of the work, and the poor conditions, and could hardly wait until the three months were up. When the contract was up, the German overseer came to the workers and said: "The Reich is engaged in a life or death struggle with the forces of the Communist-Capitalist conspiracy for world domination. The German army is making untold sacrifices of blood to safeguard the New Europe. What sort of man would shirk his duty now, and stand idly by? Only a sub-human, treacherous sort,

196

and we'll crush those with an iron fist! Friends! Who among you would object to your contracts being extended for a further six months?"

The war did not stop, the hundred lira became almost worthless, and the work was driven at an unbearable pace. Eventually, Alfonso and two or three other young men escaped and managed to get to the Italian border. When he reached Rome, they were already looking for him at his old job – the Minister of War thought he could do with an all-expenses-paid trip to Russia. But Alfonso had learned a thing or two during his time abroad, and was convinced (history later serving to underline the justice of his conviction) that his participation on the Eastern Front would not change the outcome of events one jot. He therefore retreated to this room.

The police, of course, were not so naïve as to look for the fugitive son under his mother's bed. They called Madame Pauline in for questioning, and asked her where her son was.

"Cologne," she replied, because the twins sometimes brought little bottles of it home, and this is the first place that came to mind.

Did they write to Cologne and demand Alfonso? Did the Germans ever reply? Maybe they simply gave up on him and decided to go ahead and take Moscow without him. Maybe his little card file got incinerated in the bombing. More than one person survived the war because the list on which their name figured was consumed in the flames. Dictators keep their victims on a paper chain – if the papers get lost, they lose their power over them.

Maybe in the future, things will be different. They may not keep records on paper any more, but each citizen might be required to tally every day how much his income was, how much he spent, what he did, where he was, who he talked to and what about, and then every evening a giant computer will check the facts. By midnight, they will have weeded out any contradictions, and in the morning the duty robot will come and take the source of the false reporting away to be tortured. But we're not there yet. As long as it's the fallible Italian police who are keeping track of what people think and where, there will always be people who slip through the cracks.

Alfonso disappeared. I felt we shared a common fate, common principles – and I am happy to listen to him talk about his model railway. We always talk about the model railway, because since he's been cooped up in this tiny room at the end of the corridor, he has no other topics of conversation. I understand him entirely – for, if you've satisfied the need for lunch, you need a reason to live, and if you manage to satisfy the need for dinner too, you start to need ideals. When he retired into his monastic isolation, Alfonso started to build a model railway from tin cans. It started off as a hobby, and became something deadly serious. Alfonso became a prisoner of the wheels. He thought endlessly about how to solve this or that particular problem; his sisters would go after work to look for tin cans for him, he bought welding equipment, and would be at work by the crack of dawn. I'm sure there was a time when he was afraid of the coming of peace, the day when he would have to go out into the streets again, but I think that's passed now. He knows he's never going to go back out. The daily struggle seems utterly pointless when you're working on your masterpiece, your life's work, a work that only you can finish.

And now that I've sat down, after so long, to unearth from the avalanche of years past the memory of these few days of mine, the language of the people I now live among slips away from my consciousness with the everyday realities of my neighbourhood. I'm writing in a language not a living soul within a hundred miles of me understands about people who lived and died a long way away, trying to pin down the shape of faded clouds of dust, of unfulfilled prophecies – and I feel now more than ever that Alfonso and I are kindred spirits.

"I only make tracks when I'm tired and can't think of anything new," Alfonso told me. "But even so, I've managed to find a more efficient way of making them. It all depends on how you cut the shapes from the tins."

"Yes, indeed," I affirm. "But do you know when Madame Pauline is coming back? I can't stay much longer."

"Not to worry, I'll tell her you called. But do come again soon!"

"*A bientôt!*" I say.

"And then I'll show you what I did with the locomotive!" he promises from the door.

As I step out of the gate, there's a terrific commotion. At first, I think the paratroopers have arrived and the first wave of mechanised infantry is making its way down from the *Piazza Venezia*. Then I see that it's just a police escort, honking away as usual alongside three open-topped black cars.

"Long live the Pope!" the passersby shout. "Look, it's the Pope, coming back from *San Lorenzo!*"

The Pope has clearly been fulfilling his most ancient parochial duty, as Bishop of Rome, and been too see the victims of the bombing, to offer solace, promise help, and distribute his blessings among the survivors. "He hasn't been out in the city since '39" someone next to me is saying, "it was when he went to see the king!" I too remember the event. It was in the dying days of '39, when Hitler was planning his assault against the neutrals, preparing his positions in great secrecy to strike against Denmark, Norway, Belgium, and Holland. Mussolini was saying nothing, the word "Axis" disappeared from the newspapers, and the Italians were eagerly waiting to see what Pius and Victor Emanuel would do in the interests of peace.

There was no official information, except that at the meeting there was no official reception, because Christ's representative on earth can't be seen to be eating, like mere mortals. The unofficial account of their meeting came in the form of a joke:

"Tell me Holy Father," the king asked, "what do you usually pray for in the evenings? Let me pray for the same thing, so that our prayers may coincide with each other." "My son", Pius said, "every night I ask the Lord to open those two crooks' eyes!"

"*Accidenti*, I've been asking him to close them!"

I head home. It's September, and the days are getting shorter. I hold fearfully on to the little packet of *polenta*, the bulwark of our spiritual well-being for the morrow, as I let myself be carried away in the flow of humanity in the narrow streets. The door of the Pantheon is now closed. From here, I have to cut across to the end of Baboon Street.

I run through my day in my mind. I wonder what the others are thinking about right now? Becker must be thinking that he'll stay here and switch sides. He draws a parallel between the mood in Carthage following Scipio's entry into Rome and the mood prevailing currently in Berlin. Figaro is thinking how it would be if Mussolini came to his shop for a shave, if the Duce leaned back in his chair and stuck his neck out, presenting his protruding adam's apple. Diana is thinking whether it's worth the effort and the sacrifice of the rigmarole with the smoky charcoal stove for the sake of heating up the beans. Eckstein that the Prussian Generals could this very night turn against the Führer, Alfonso about his trains... and the Pope? Perhaps he's thinking about his last visit to the city – what if he'd done things differently, then? Or maybe he's thinking about the bodies lying under the bricks in *San Lorenzo*. Or maybe even that two official copies of a document exist, bearing two signatures at the end – Pacelli and Hitler. The Concordat he signed in the summer of 1933, which enhanced the Nazis' prestige, and undermined Dollfuss. Little Dollfuss, who they say needed a ladder to pick redcurrents, and who died for Austria with lead in his spine. Signed in Munich, not so far from Dachau... its nascent crown of thorns, the wire and the whips were already in place, then. Or maybe he's thinking of Ribbentrop's gold-embroidered swastika as he sat facing him in his private study.

The colonel is certainly thinking of Ariane, and Ariane is certainly not thinking of the colonel.

"I didn't re-heat the beans," Diana says.

"That's ok, they're fine cold too."

The stillness of the night is once more shattered, the windows open. There's a palpable buzz, like on the twenty-fifth of July, but it's softer, more excited. The radio says audibly: "The Allied forces and Italy have signed an armistice."

"The situation..." I say, but Diana checks me. "Play something, instead," she says.

This night, we can safely light a candle, even in our little glass house, for there's been an armistice. The flying fortresses are not looking for our light in the window. I open

200

the second volume of the *Well-tempered Clavier* at random, and I make my own separate peace with our sorry century as I reach for something painless and enduring. The candle's flame and Diana listen to the music immobile, even to the last cadence, the final flourish.

Every new-born day, like every new-born person, has its own particular face. The great advantage of our little glass home is that even from bed, I can already look the day's clouds in the eye, and from their shape and movement, can decide what weather will prevail. For Rome's days are governed by the winds and breezes. They are not nameless currents of air, as in other places, where they are merely "Easterly" or "Southerly", but – as any foreigner who has sailed these shores will have learned – have their proper names; from the East, it is the *Bora* that blows, while from the South, the *Sirocco*. The visitor just getting acquainted with the city will find in St Peter's square the marble ring that has all the names of the ancient winds carved on it. The Roman greets a scrap of cloud rushing South in an otherwise blue sky like an old acquaintance – the *Tramontana* has arrived!

This Northerly wind rushes at the city across the *Ponte Milvio*, sweeping the *Piazza del Popolo* as it goes. Then dividing into three, heads right to the tomb of the Emperor Augustus, whistling along the narrow streets; runs down the *Corso*, that long, straight road where once wild riderless horses raced, blows into the windows of the *Palazzo Venezia* (into the great, empty hall where formerly the Austro-Hungarian delegates to the Holy See played ping-pong, then later the Duce did his Napoleon impression); and finally runs from left to right down Baboon Street, hot on the heels of the paratroopers who came yesterday. This wind blows through the tunnel under the *Quirinale*, caresses the places where Maecenas' garden used to be, and then – with a great leap – follows the line of the cemeteries built by Appius Caecus to the cemeteries of tomorrow, or in other words – the front.

It's light, and I wake Diana.

"The *Tramontana* has arrived!"

She turns to me, and says sleepily:

"Go get bread."

I know the bread will be poor, and the news will not be any better, but nonetheless I step out into the hostile world. On the fourth floor, a dishevelled head pokes out at me:

"That crook's sprung him out of jail!"

On the second, I hear a different version:

"That crook's escaped!"

It takes less than a minute at the baker's to clear up the meaning of these various commentaries on current affairs. The "crook" on the fourth floor refers to Adolf Hitler, *Reichs-kancellar*, Leader of the SA, Supreme Head of the German Armed Forces, while the "crook" on the second refers to Benito Mussolini, Founder of the Empire, The Duce of Fascism, knight of the Order of the Most Holy Annunciation, Honorary cousin to the King, and Honorary Corporal of the Fascist Militia.

"Where was he? He wasn't in the *Regina Coeli* with all the people he'd had locked up, was he?"

"He was on the *Gran Sasso*, in *Abruzzo*, in the ski-lodge!"

"A king is a king, even in hell," I say to myself, in Hungarian.

"Hitler sent some paratroopers and took him away in a funny little contraption."

"He needn't have bothered," someone interposed, "he's got Rome in his pocket with its six divisions to boot, he could simply have told him to take a taxi down to town!"

"Yes, but this was more dramatic. Journalists need to live too."

"Badoglio could have taken him along to the Allies."

"I suppose he forgot to pack him in the heat of the moment!"

The sermon is crowned with its traditional "amen": *Che vadano morire ammazzati! – they should drop dead, the lot of them!*

Diana's up when I get back, and listens to my news as she divides yesterday's leftover *faricello* for us.

"What's going to happen now?"

"Germany puts the clock back," I say, quoting the title of Mowrer's book. "Mowrer explains Hitler's rise to power by saying he simply pushed the hands on the clock-face of history back. He wiped away Weimar and Versailles, and kept go-

202

ing, back to the Middle Ages with the yellow stars, and on into antiquity with the swastika. Mowrer describes how the students stood outside the university chanting *Wir scheissen auf die Freiheit.*

"So?"

"Don't you see? That's what's happening right now. Hitler has put the clock back. He's bringing back Mussolini. Mussolini's going to go straight back into the ping-pong hall of the *Palazzo Venezia.* The Fascists will simply get together again and appoint him Prime Minister. And then Mussolini will put the clock back, too. He'll tell the Allies that the armistice is off, and what will Eisenhower care, he's hardly had any use out of it anyway. Ossobuco will re-open his sculptor's workshop, the former ministers will come out of hiding in the monasteries and go back to their desks, and army officers will dig out their old uniforms from wherever they hid them..."

"No!' Diana shouts. "No! You can't undo history."

"Why not?"

"Because there's not enough glue in the world to make the broken statues whole! Mussolini can't come back!"

"He might be here already!"

"He won't come back, and I'll tell you why: because more than being a journalist, he's an actor, and not a bad one at that. And the proof of that is not his clowning around dressed up as a miner, or a peasant, or a pilot, or even a general, but that he knows his audience. He knows when they'll throw rotten eggs at him, and he won't come out on stage."

"I think he'll reprise his Julius Caesar!"

"No, he'll go somewhere he can still expect applause – somewhere in Germany."

"I think he'll be back. Not that he misses Rome so much, but he misses his balcony. Mussolini never went to Abyssinia – he only ever saw the Empire from his balcony. Stepping out onto the red carpet (as the Pope steps out onto the loggia of St Peter's), filled him with some high-priestly or ship's-captainly pride. Wasn't it he who called the corner of the *Palazzo Chigi* the prow of the ship of state? I think, come darkness, when no-one's looking, he'll go back out onto his balcony and, hands on hips, thrust his chin once more out over the *Piazza Venezia...*"

"What you should really do is go into town and find out what's going on!"

"I'll tell you now, we're having *faricello* and history for lunch yet again."

Going down, going out into the street is a mission, a hunt for money and food. But today I have an added task – I have to gather information to see what direction we should point our little glass ship in, because it might be (though I daren't admit it out loud) three or four weeks until the Fifth and Eighth armies arrive with the solution to our problems. For now, it's the Gestapo and the paratroopers (but not Ariane's ones, sadly) who are in charge here. Baboon Street is now a section of the front, and it's time to find out where the enemy are located.

Mussolini got out. Outside the central post office, with typical German efficiency, they are even now putting up his life-sized photographs on either side of the door, wearing a steel helmet and looking up and right into the sky, as if wondering if that over there is the rescue plane come to free him. I remember that on the very same spot on the 26th July, the day after his fall, a well-dressed gentleman stood, holding a massive, old-fashioned spear. The (prematurely) ecstatic Romans speared their torn-down images of Mussolini onto its point, merrily, without malice, as if they'd spent the last twenty years doing nothing but waiting for this man with his spear to come. And he had surely been preparing his weapon for this very moment for years...

"Mussolini in Munich!" a newspaper vendor shouts. "Read the Führer's speech!"

Yes, it was right here that the man with the spear had stood, but Germany's managed to turn back the clock.

I start for the library, more out of habit than anything else. Events belong in certain time-categories. The events of today will only attain any real weight years from now as far as the library is concerned. First, it will penetrate via the journals, then the books themselves, and all that will be left of its mood is what makes it inside those walls. If I should walk this way again in twenty years, I'll go and see if anyone has noted that the image of the Duce has reclaimed the space of the Patient Lancer. For the moment though, I'm just looking for a friend to assure me, "yes, in fourteen days, they'll be here."

It's the archaeologist who comes my way, fighting against the *Tramontana*. I wonder which event of the Punic Wars he'll liken today's news to.

"And so he's out and he'll start all over again," he sighs. "Everyone's talking about Napoleon's hundred days. Nothing of the sort! If only because no-one went to fetch Napoleon from Elba by plane! The only thing *Bagnasciuga*[2] and Napoleon have in common is that they leave behind them countless dead and as many newly-made barons, counts, and princes."

"This time, they'll abolish titles! You don't really think that Ciano, Grandi and the rest will stay counts?!"

"But of course! Otherwise, the Pacelli family would also have to give up its princely rank, and there's no question of that happening! But that's beside the point. The only person who ever compared Mussolini to Napoleon is Mussolini himself, and that's why he lived on the *Foro Bonaparte* back in Milan when he was just a journalist."

"I thought he said he was the reincarnation of the Emperor Augustus."

"What a laugh. You can see how little he knows of Roman history. I wonder if you can guess who's being described if I quote something to you: '*cuius rei lubet simulator ac dissimulator, alieni appetens, sui profusus, ardens in cupiditatibus; satis eloquentiae, sapientia parum*[3]'."

"From antiquity?"

"Catiline!"

---

[2] a naval term that Mussolini used incorrectly in his 1943 speech before the Allied invasion, and which then became his derogatory nickname

[3] Both a dissimulator and a dissembler as it suited, jealous of the property of others, spendthrift with his own, consumed with desires; acceptably eloquent, but lacking wisdom

"Poor Catiline! All that remains of his life is Cicero's slanders. What would be left of us if all that were remembered was the closing argument for the prosecution?"

"You're entirely mistaken. I was quoting Sallust. You may remember that Sallust was no friend of Cicero's. He disliked in him the *homo novus*, probably that Greek style of Latinity which for so long was called 'classical'. But that's beside the point. The fact is that they both agreed that Catiline was a crook. They speak only of conspiracies, while it might be more accurate to say that he founded a party. Or perhaps it's even more accurate to think of the blackshirts as a conspiracy. What did Catiline want? To get to Rome – *Marcia su Roma*. He, too, started from Tuscany, but unfortunately for him Facta was not Prime Minister, or Consul in Rome, and he got arrested. I have a small monograph on the subject lying in a drawer, but its time will come. Sallust's description of the members of Catiline's party, those ancient fascists is timely and accurate: 'the shameless, libertine, and profligate, who had dissipated their patrimonies by gambling, gluttony, and sensuality; who had contracted heavy debts to purchase immunity for their crimes or offenses; assassins and the sacrilegious from all around, convicted or dreading conviction for their evil deeds; all whom their tongue or their hand maintained by perjury or civil bloodshed; all, in fine, whom wickedness, poverty, or a guilty conscience disquieted, were the associates and intimate friends of Catiline'... I can quote it by heart, because I've been studying them for the last twenty years!"

At this point, my companion looked over at the photograph of Catiline in his steel helmet.

"Do you know what we call people like that in Italian? *La teppa!* – *rabble*. If Sallust, who is the master of brief epithets, had known this expression, he would have said nothing more than: *La teppa!*"

"If I remember rightly, senators and patricians took part in the Catiline conspiracy, too."

"Maybe they did. Mussolini counted on others too – the opportunists and the idiots. He had it painted on the walls of every house: 'Fight, obey, believe!' That went for all his followers: the *teppa* fought, the opportunists obeyed, and the idiots believed... and they all glorified him. That's why he lasted so long, that's why he can start again now, only this time even the idiots know what's going on, the opportunists have allied themselves with the Allies, and poor Catiline can only count on the *teppa.*"

We both turn our backs to the wind and the dictator, as the archaeologist continues: "There is one difference between them, though. Catiline, when he saw that his troops were beaten, rushed at his enemies and fell, while this pitiful crook marched around in a steel helmet for twenty years, until they toppled him in a top hat, and now he's marching around in a steel helmet again, waiting for the day they string him up in his civvies!"

"Let's hope he won't have long to wait!" I say, with all my heart.

"I can't wait to publish my book on historical analogies!"

"*Magari,*" I say. If only.

I like Rome. I like it, because I know that its drawers are home to books and memoirs waiting to be liberated. I like it because I'm no longer an alien here – if I walk from the main post office to the library, I'm sure to meet a familiar face. When I do, I can be sure that we're on the same wavelength. But what's even better is that I can guess the thoughts of strangers, too. I know exactly what the people who saw the photo of the Duce in his steel helmet this morning were thinking, what they'd like to do, and I am pleased to be part of the majority. I first felt a part of the majority when the soles of my shoes started developing holes and my feet got wet in the rain, because most people wear shoes this bad. But this feeling is different – now even the stranger is part of my conspiracy. We are just as hungry as each another and we share one big, common, desire. When I was still going around door to door, house to house, taking people's blood pressure, I learned that on days like this, people's blood pressure shoots up, and their varicose veins start acting up again. Once again, I feel that my finger is on the pulse.

I like Rome, it's my Bakony – its great libraries are the bastions of free thinking. Their walls resist the slush of the news-

207

papers and periodicals, trapdoors wait to bury the fascist literature. The libraries' watchword is Europe for the Europeans. I read somewhere about factories that kept working even after the heaviest bombing, but which were brought to a halt when the offices of the management were hit. The library is the office of the management of European culture. What a ridiculous thing it is to say that something "disappears into the library"! It's the things that stay unwritten, never noted down, that disappear. The library is the eternal present. *Scriptum est, ergo est!*

I like the library, and I'm proud that I can find the book I'm looking for among the hundreds of thousands of others. The process is somewhat similar to playing one of the truly great organs, or when a man is trying to find the woman who's made for him in a city of a million people. Books, like their readers, have their own destinies – and it really all depends on when they meet.

I like the studious old men, these very rich men, who pore over their books in eternal peace. There are those among them, here in Rome, who have read twenty or thirty thousand. There are those who check whether the Sanskrit has been correctly rendered into Chinese, those who can transcribe a fragment of a Greek play from a scrap of papyrus with thirty little characters on it. These are the people who help me place current events into context.

And, after the rows of German paratroopers, it's good to be able to grab on to what is truly eternal in Rome.

Of my friends in the library, today I find only Jator Apaitiz. Since he's a priest, I once asked him:

"What about the omniscience of God? If God knows everything in advance, what then of free will? And if the will isn't free, then why did God make this place such a miserable one?"

"My son," he replied, "that is a question for a novice. An elderly priest like myself should only be concerned with keeping himself out of hell." And since he's a Basque priest, he added, "And Basque men should see to it that Franco gets there as soon as possible!"

"The professors of Roman law and the great experts of Canon law at the university of Bologna spent a hundred years debating," Apaitiz greets me by saying, "what would have happened if Lazarus, after he had risen from the dead, had made another will. The question was whether he had any right to make a second will at all, and whether that will would be valid. This, today, has become a question of state. Does a political corpse, if they bring it back to life, have the right to play dictator again?"

I know what my Basque friend is secretly thinking and I rise to the occasion: "Maybe he hasn't quite earned his place in the boiling sulphur yet. Perhaps in His infinite wisdom, God has granted him another month or two here on Earth, to make sure he won't get off lightly with the cleansing fires of purgatory in the next life!"

"They've robbed ten million people of at least thirty years of their lives so that these two criminals could each scratch another five. Eternal damnation is not punishment enough for those three hundred million lost years!"

Apaitiz closes his eyes for a moment, and imagines himself atop a snow-white cloud, looking down on the smoky fires of hell far below. I like Apaitiz, and I have every faith in his little private vision. I picture beside him the tall, quiet, raven-haired Basque waif who opened the door when I came to treat his pneumonia, and whom he called "my little sister".

"Have you heard, they've sunk the *Roma*."

"Yes, but that's not the main thing."

"I think it is. Not, of course, from the point of view of the newspapers, or even of our daily lives. But from the point of view of world history, it's a grave and sad event indeed: the sinking of the last of the Catholic navies!"

"This war…"

"Yes, I know, this war doesn't look like a war of religions. But, just by chance, it's now that a question almost half a millennium old has been decided – who rules the waves? The question was straightforward on dry land – the old Roman *limes* was still there to separate the Catholic world from the Protestant. The *limes* – for the Romans would only go as far as the vines would grow. The Romans liked wine, they knew that life is good when there are grapes that grow. And the vine is the fruit of Catholicism. The Protestants, as their punishment, must endure – even in this life – having nothing but beer or whisky to drink. But there's no such demarcation on the sea – there, it's absolute war that decides. The Catholic fleets were out of luck."

"But they say that the Virgin appeared at Lepanto and decided the battle in their favour!"

"That was against the Turks, not against the Protestants. Against them, she didn't even bother protecting our Great Armada. Trafalgar and Aboukir were Catholic losses, too. The Americans ended up taking the Philippines and Cuba from Spain, and now the British have finished off the French fleet at Oran. There was nothing left but the Italian, the poor little Italian fleet, which tried to look after its ships. The *Litoris* got torpedoed every time she left port. The *Roma* never left port at all, and when at last she did, she sank. The Protestants rule the sea!"

"But the Japanese…"

"That's nothing but a passing phase. A historical anomaly. The yellow races, like the Germans, can count on nothing but the initial, passing, success of surprise. I keep telling you, you're missing the point. The point is that in the space of a decade, all three Catholic Great Powers have disappeared. The French, because of their left-wing government, the Italians because of their fascist dictator, and Spain because that cursed Franco brought all the suffering of fascism and civil war down on our heads! But I know that the form of state is nothing but an external factor, and when the time comes for things to happen, they will happen anyway."

In the library, every conversation is really nothing more than an exchange of monologues. But from time to time, the subjects of these separate monologues somehow intersect. This is where Jator Apaitiz's thoughts meet my own.

"The bombs fell just at the very moment when several historical processes met – the exhaustion of the army, the boredom of the king, the Germans' ire, the suspiciousness of the

Allies – and the steady hand of a German pilot let fly those bombs just as if he had found the right note on a piano."

"The Church must change her foreign policy!" sighs Apaitiz. "If there's no longer a single Catholic monarch, nor a Catholic fleet left, the world is not the same. This despite the prediction of St Malachius, who said that our present Pope, the "*Pastor Angelicus*" would be followed by a naval Pope, a "*Pastor et nauta*"! In any case, we should see what Nostradamus says."

"Next time," I reply quickly, because it comes back to me that I came here looking for facts, not opinions and prophecies. Better to go see Figaro in the street of the rosary makers.

Stepping out the door, I turn to face the *Tramontana*. The outside world is something other than the hothouse of ideas inside the yard-thick walls. But here, facing the stern façade of the *Collegium Romanum*, it's not quite the same as the city the Germans have just occupied, either. This Rome cannot be penetrated by the fleeting politics of the day. The square of Saint Ignatius will forever resemble the stageset for a Rossini opera, and you can't drive tanks down its wings. From here to the Pantheon, the *palazzi* form an exclusive union – membership is open only to those whose stones bear the weight of at least three centuries. Many were seminaries or convents which, though now home to mortal men who do things very much of the flesh, have – just as a priest is blessed and becomes *sacerdos in aeternum* – managed to preserve the indelible face of the innocence of their sainted youth. Walking down the narrow streets, you feel the weight and protection of their walls.

With a little detour, I can go through the *Santa Maria sopra Minerva*, Rome's only Gothic temple. This is where Fra Angelico, that divine artist, master of the sky-blue Madonnas, is buried. On his tombstone – miraculously, they say – there's always a freshly-cut flower. I'd like to see if it's still there, despite the carpet bombing, the German grenades and Mussolini.

Entering by the little back door, I come straight to the large, weighty sarcophagus of an inquisitor. Facing it is the

211

artist's plain tombstone, and the flower – though hardly fresh – is indeed there, white against the modest stone habit of the painter-friar.

Few people pass behind the Pantheon. Even the cats are gone, though they are the guardians of the ancient ruins. The huge bronze doors are shut. It pops into my mind that this is where the kings of Italy lie in wait for resurrection day. Perhaps the reason they've closed the doors is that the cautious guards are worried that someone might come and tell the first Victor Emmanuel what's happened to the last. The Abruzzan peasants have disappeared, too, who always meet here when they come up to Rome. They, in their groups, bring something of the countryside to the heart of Rome. But the happy days are gone when they would be here, discussing the life and death questions of lambs and cheese... and so are the lambs and the cheese.

From here, it's spitting distance to the French church of Saint Louis, but this is closed, too. It's trying to do what the Maginot line failed to do, and keep the Germans out. I know that beyond its doors is France. Until the city fell, this is where all the self-respecting atheists came for Sunday mass. It was good to be able to listen to the organ next to Poussin's grave (because every Roman church is a veritable cemetery, too), waiting for the choirmaster, Vignanelli, to lift our souls up to heaven with an expansive Bach fugue, and picture the moment when Tisserand, the paunchy, bearded French cardinal (who had himself been a cavalry officer) would celebrate a Te Deum after the final victory of the Allies, while the Moroccans' brass band would play the Marseillaise beneath the arches.

On the left, the guards have disappeared from outside the Senate building. I feel like a freshly-arrived traveller, trying to see everything in his Baedekker. I go and see, therefore, whether the famous relief is still in the courtyard, the one depicting "Mussolini offering the King the Imperial Crown of Abyssinia". They say that it was the tailor of one of the ministers, Bottai, who made it. During a fitting, the minister noticed that the tailor's workshop was full of little statues, and that the good tailor skilfully reproduced the features of the fascist grandees and his more distinguished clients, so he ordered the statue for the Senate building from him. It might just be an urban legend, but the little marble uniforms do have carefully pressed trousers and well-cut button-holes. The diminutive king stands on a platform, waiting for the steel-helmeted Duce to give him his bauble, while Badoglio, Graziani and De Bono look on on horseback. There's a wooden cover now over the relief, as if they were trying to protect it from the bombing, but I know that there was no such cover on it when they were actually still bombing the city. The real question now is whether they've covered it today because it's got the king on it, or whether they covered it up yesterday to hide Mussolini. Or maybe they knocked that prominent jaw off here, too, that wonderful night in July? In the times we live in, statues have a shorter lifespan than people!

On my way to see Figaro, I have to cut across the *Piazza Navona*. The big square, now the plaything of the wind, was built on the ruins of a *circus*, and still retains its outline. Scraps of yesterday's news roll in the wind from one fountain to the other. The distinctive baroque forms of the fountains are awaiting the liberation under heavy concrete blocks. Bernini's nereids are very wisely sleeping through the war.

It's good to look up at the sky, which – after the narrow streets that reveal only thin strips of it – opens up over the square. Past the *piazza*, I already feel at home, because here I've been to almost every house, knocked on many doors, and heard the beating of many a local heart. You move differently through a neighbourhood where you know the insides of the houses, where you've been over the thresholds, and where you know that someone will give you shelter if the rains come, or the Gestapo.

In the square, the welcome feeling of being on familiar ground warms me. "I'll have to look in on Miss Lucia and see how she is," I think, looking up at a window behind which lives one of my favourite patients.

She's a lovely, spirited, lively woman, and the only reason Diana doesn't grudge me our long talks is that she turned seventy-five last year. She sat at her window looking out onto the square so long that she finally decided to research and write its history, a curious thought in someone over fifty who's never written before. Not so curious, though, if you consider that Rome always draws its travellers and admirers back in time. "Everything is connected to everything else," Miss Lucia says, "and a single drop holds the entire ocean. Everything is reflected in the *Piazza Navona*, and if someone had lived a thousand years here, they would know all there is to know." She's right, too: in the flooded *circus*, they replayed the naval victories of imperial Rome, on its sands bled the martyrs, in its death-row cells their chapels were consecrated (like that of *San Agnese*, facing Miss Lucia's window), and when the invaders overran Rome, it was over this *circus* that they ran. This is where the Dorias, who were the lords of Genoa, built their palace, and the Massimos, in whose house Saint Filippo Neri resurrected a young, dead, prince; one corner of the Braschi's (a Papal family) palace overlooks the square, too, which was once up for grabs in a lottery for a farthing, sank to the depths of housing the offices of the fascist party, and through whose windows the chimneys of the stoves of the bombed-out residents of San Lorenzo now protrude.

Miss Lucia has picked her topic well, and her decade in the archives was well spent. Eventually, she wrote her own story into the history of the square, and she could finally record the people she herself had met. She had been the wife of Van Gogh's dealer in Berlin. Rilke and Lou Andreas Salome used to visit them to admire *outré* French drawings ("they sat in a corner, giggling, the girl dressed outrageously, Rilke in white cufflinks. I went over there and threw them out, let them cavort someplace else! Rilke, in any case, looked like a very well-dressed three-day-old corpse"). Miss Lucia was the owner of the very first copy of *Buddenbrooks*.

The people I know... do I really know the people from whose lives I can recount an anecdote or two? Or whose writings I've read a little of, or whose faces I've known, or a single day of their lives? Maybe I would know them if I spent a lifetime studying their lives. All I know now is that in this narrow street that leads to Figaro's there lives a Polish patient of mine. Thirty years ago, he got engaged, but his bride-to-be fell ill. On her deathbed, she made him promise to look after her ailing aged mother. The old lady is ninety now, her al-most-son-in-law sixty, but he's kept his word. They sit and starve together and from time to time rehash their memories of the Poland of the last century. This is where Pompeio lives, too, who's a real Roman, and was the concierge at the Austro-Hungarian Embassy to the Holy See, and who was almost the subject of a diplomatic spat after the dissolution of the dual monarchy. For he chose Hungary and, by a legal quirk, spent his entire life on Hungarian soil without ever having left Rome. He doesn't speak a word of the language, but some-how understands every conversation. Here's the home of the Austrian bishop whose role-model is Hindenburg. On his desk is a cross, while above it an oil portrait of Hindenburg hangs, looking – with his odd assortment of decorations – onto the endless library of works on the exegesis of the New Testament. Over there lives the French priest whose days and years are dedicated to collecting evidence and proving be-yond doubt that the portrait of the Madonna in the porphyry-coated church of the Alsatians wept several times in the 18th century, shedding real tears. Over there is the workshop of the last *sventolatore*, or fan-maker, whose trade is to take feath-ers and from them make that essential tool of the Vestal vir-gins, the fan to stoke a charcoal fire. He's a good sort, and I can picture him fantasising as he works about how Beelzebub will one day fan the everlasting embers under il Duce's cauldron. I also happen to know that the coachmaker, carrying on his dying trade beneath the arches of one of the ancient buildings, repairing the old horse-drawn carriages, is a police informer. This alternative career of his is a secret, but everybody in the neighbourhood knows not to talk to him about anything but the weather.

And I know that there are not only streets here, but roofs as well, on which people live and feed their chickens. One of them even has huge vines on it, and I once ate a bunch of grapes grown on a Roman rooftop. Ageing felines and well-guarded young ladies plan their romantic escapades there, and if il Duce has been toppled, or if the enemy have marched into town, the news spreads from rooftop to rooftop like the winged Easterly *Tramontana*. Behind the *Piazza Navona*, we go even further back in time, another couple of centuries. The last time that the *landsknecht* (the halberded ancestors of today's paratroopers) were here, in Benvenuto Cellini's time, they forgot to raze these streets. Figaro was right to come to the street of the rosary-makers when he got fed up with the spirit of our century. Everything's relative. Standing beneath the ancient towers, the twenty years of fascism and the thousand promised of the Third Reich seem equally insignificant.

Figaro's shop is closed, as if to shut out today's calamitous news. In any event, I knock: three long, one short, the call sign of the BBC. Figaro's eyes appear in the spyhole, and then the door opens.

"Come in, we're in here."

Apart from our clever little friend, I see two boys I don't know, and the darkness that once more envelops the place as the door is shut behind me quickly swallows them up. For a while, all I hear is their voices, until my eyes adjust to the scanty light of the candle burning beneath the image of the Madonna.

"They're good boys," Figaro says in the dark.

"What happened?" I ask, coming straight to the point.

No one replies. It's not an easy question. If something happens in Singapore, then the answer is simple – the BBC tells you what's happened, and we extrapolate on our mental chessboards, pushing the troops here and there, debating the likely weather forecast, and deciding on the most probable next two or three moves. But this time, we're the pawns, and we can all feel that we're in a poor position.

"How did the Germans get in?" I ask, more forcefully. "How?"

The little clever one answers.

"By train. Simple as that, in their civvies. The same as they went into Norway. As tourists. Our officers, our trained officer corps spent forty-five days figuring out how to protect Rome from every possible angle. In the meanwhile, the German tourists occupied the Hotel Continental and when they heard we'd made a separate peace, changed their nightgowns for uniforms, put their submachine guns together, and started firing out the window."

The first of the unknown boys takes up the story.

"I was just saying. People were walking down the *Via Veneto*, and there was a full-blown battle raging outside the Continental. There were soldiers and civilians shooting at the windows, but the soldiers were from the most random units, practically no two had the same uniform. I saw an old man who got behind a tree and let off at least ten shots with his hunting rifle. 'That's all the rounds I had' he said, and calmly went home. There were a few dead women and children in the square, too, but they looked so unreal."

At this point, the second unknown boy takes over, like in Shakespeare when a long narration is sometimes split between two or three characters. "It was the same on the *Via Nazionale*. People were walking along while the war was fought around them. On one side of the street was the audience of passers-by, while on the other someone threw a bomb at the Germans, who were also walking along, from a car. Then our soldiers came, running, bloody, saying that all was lost, while there were trucks going the other way taking fresh troops to the front line, somewhere near the Protestant cemetery. There was a German tank approaching from the direction of the Opera which stuck its snout in here and there and then left."

"The Street of Baboons was shelled too, from afar, with a small-caliber gun," I say, just so that I have something to bring to the conversation. "I heard the Germans came over from Sardinia."

"Not a bit of it! They were all stationed down at Ostia's and the Castellis', waiting for the order to advance."

"The problem was that the populace wasn't armed," Figaro says calmly. "We'd have dealt with them. The Party leaders – Gallo, who came over from the island of Ventotene, and the others who got out on September the eighth told the army, plain as day: 'Give us guns!' That evening, they handed out guns and hand-grenades in the barracks, but in the morning the police came and took whatever they found. Fascist lot! Never mind, the Party will deal with them, too!"

"Which party?" I ask clumsily. 'The Party' here has meant the fascist party for the last twenty years.

"Why, the Communist Party!"

"Are you a communist?"

"Well, I don't know if I'm really a communist, but I do know that I'm certainly an anti-fascist, and I know enough to know that that's enough. The communists have always, everywhere, been the best anti-fascists!"

"I didn't even know the Communist Party existed here."

"But of course it does! Didn't you hear that enormous explosion after the bombing, when the Liberators had left? That was the boys blowing up the munitions dump to celebrate the formation of the Party!"

"The trouble is," the clever little man says, "that there isn't one Communist Party in Rome today, there's about twenty-five. Everyone wants their own party here!"

"So tell me, who's going to make order here, then?"

"We will, the socialists! There's a tradition of socialism here, and in this place, you can't even cut hair or shave without traditions. Who are these communists, anyway?"

The darkened barbershop really has the effect of being a hidey-hole for underground parties, and I suspect that the two unknown boys are members, if not leaders, of some new party.

"Who are they? I'll tell you who," Figaro says. "The people they took as volunteers to Spain, or hired them to go to Africa and took them to Malaga instead. The poor sods who made it back from Russia and saw how good the Russian people really are. The Germans would hit our soldier's hands with the butts of their rifles when they wanted to cling on to the retreating trucks, while the Russians shared their last crust of bread with them. The people who did the fighting here were communist partisans. The rest were just bystanders. It's the same in France, it's only the communists who stand up, risk their hides and do the shooting. Or do you really think the priests are storing up hand-grenades?"

He stands up, lifts the lid of the box he's been sitting on, and gestures: "Thirty of them. We'll use them when the day comes."

"I'd like to be a communist, too, when that day comes," I say.

"And what about today?"

"Today, I'm an anarchist," I admit. "I don't like the state, I've never worn a uniform, never paid tax, and I'm for peace. I want to throw these grenades at the people I'm angry at."

"That's all right by us. We're willing to work with anyone who's an anti-fascist, even if it's the king himself!"

"The king's scarpered," the second unknown boy says.

"Quite right, too," responds the clever little one. "The last twenty years everyone's been shouting 'long live the King!' Even the sailors on the sinking ships would shout 'long live the King' before they threw themselves to the sharks. For once, he's listened to the will of his people and he's gone off to live."

"They shouted 'long live Mussolini' too!"

"And he's still alive, isn't he? He got out!"

"Pardon me, he didn't get out, Hitler got him out."

"So, what's the difference?"

"If he'd got out, he'd be back here, taking up where he left off. He'd play tennis in the morning, have his picture taken in a variety of uniforms during lunch, and in the evenings he'd go and see the Petacci woman to read the papers and have a good time. By reading the papers, he'd find out that all was well, and could snore peacefully till morning between his sheets, which the BBC says are blue. But the master won't let him! He dragged him off to Germany! He's a cunning one, that Hitler."

The clever little one is another master of the popular game of 'what if'. There's no way we could get through our current misery without the occasional game of 'what if', or 'if only', or 'when the time comes'. All of a sudden, huge vistas open up in which living is a worthwhile pursuit, or rather, it would be, if only…

"If he let him come home, so Hitler must be thinking, he might go over to the Allies like his king – after all they've been doing things together for twenty years. What, you think the Allies would hang him? Did they hang Hess when he flew over? He's sitting in some English manor, and I have no doubt there's room to spare. And I have no doubt that *Bagniascuga* would be capable of it. He'd fly right over there, and explain to them how he's been an anti-fascist since the start. He'd show them his old Social Democratic Party membership card!"

Figaro joins in the fun: "You see? He doesn't have a Communist Party membership card either!"

I join in too. "Whether they'd hang him or not, I don't know, but I'm sure he'd be capable of flying over there. You mustn't forget that he's a journalist. Every journalist is convinced that whatever he writes is read next day by the whole world, and forgotten again the day after. Anyway, if he comes back, he can stay, the Allies will be here in two weeks anyway!"

The clever little one is always contradicting people. "It doesn't look like it. I think they've installed themselves on the beach at Salerno and are waiting to see what happens. They haven't even reached Naples yet! And I can understand why – Eisenhower must be saying to himself, why should I make all the effort when Italy still has a million soldiers left?"

"If he was waiting for us to throw the Germans out, then why bomb us day and night? He knocked the stuffing out of us with his Liberators, so how does he expect us to fight?" bursts out the first unknown boy.

The little clever man returns to his favourite theme, because after all everyone has their own personal way of explaining the secret logic of events, whether they picked it up in the library, or somewhere else...

"Eisenhower is a professional soldier. Ergo he's an idiot. What he learned in the military academy was that you bomb your enemy until he pleads for terms. They didn't teach him what to do in this case, when the Germans are sitting on our hands!" He continues after a brief pause. "Of course Badoglio is no better. He learned that in order to seek terms, you have to send an emissary with a little white flag, and he probably spent his forty-five days looking for a flag clean enough."

"Badoglio was afraid," Figaro says. "He was afraid of the British, he was afraid of the Germans, but most of all, he was afraid of the people sweeping him away along with the king and his little fascist friends."

"*Poveri noi!* O, poor benighted us!" the first unknown boy sighs, and then adds, "I'm hungry."

The word "hungry" echoes in every cell of my body. I can feel that I, too, am incredibly hungry. There is a kind of hunger that is beyond a feeling, and is something else altogether – a wall between us and the world. There are such walls of mist. Sometimes an indescribable migraine will come between us and external reality. The Gestapo knows full well that there is that unimaginable level of pain that one can inflict on a healthy body that will divide a person from his fellow human beings or his principles. There's no way to explain the wall of hunger away – you have to eat.

I leave quickly, exchanging the dusky calm for the stormy brightness, to find something to soothe my burning hunger. "Hunger causes hunger burns," I think to myself, "and these have to be treated with oil or fat." I'd like a piece of bacon above all else.

The *Tor di Nona* is close, I go there. I'm convinced that Catiline and Mussolini are similar also in their predilection for smoked bacon. Maybe Mussolini, free once more, is stuffing his abcessed stomach with smoked bacon as we speak... which can only be doing him good, since we usually spread fatty creams on wounds, too. The question is sure to unite the seamen of the Protestant and Catholic navies, too, and generals Alexander and Eisenhower no doubt have bacon and eggs for breakfast. Now I understand why they feel no especial hurry to reach us here, in the *Tor di Nona*... but now I don't understand why there are ideological battles raging when everyone agrees on the most important things.

The black market has disappeared again. Mussolini being at large once more is as bad as a bombing. And why not, after all? In one doorway, someone's selling a wet, white cheese – you can't save that for another day, because it goes off. This cheese – called *casciotta* – is our trusty companion on dramatic occasions. I put my entire fortune into a triangle of cheese. *Apres ce fromage le deluge!*

I rush home with my prize, quickly, lest I start nibbling it on the way. I'm convinced that people won't be the same again after the war, that they'll sit down to eat differently than they did before. During the course of our lives, now and then, one of our faculties leaves us and accompanies us no further on our journey. Now and then is a love like no other after it, and it leaves something behind in place of the faculty that nursed it... around our fortieth year, the faculty that allowed us to write poetry tends to leave us... during times of famine, something breaks in the mechanism of the mind, or of the stomach, or in that mysterious "cavern under the bedroom of our brain" – the hypothalamus, and from that time on, the immemorial fear of starvation stubbornly turns hunger into fear, makes a holy festival of every meal, and draws a halo around the bacon. The symbol of peace is the olive branch; the seed that nourishes, its oil that eases hunger-burns represent happiness. Laurels only add an interesting flavour, and are inessential. It's good to be holding some cheese in one's hands.

Diana is waiting for me in the costume of a Vestal virgin – her hands and face are sooty, and her eyes pricked by the smoke. Her right wrist hangs in exhaustion, because she's been fanning the embers so much.

"The charcoal's no good, it's wet. They soak it in water to make it heavier."

The smoke of the useless charcoal covers the world just as effectively as hunger.

"The special for today is *faricello* with cabbage!"

"Wherever did you get cabbages?"

"I'm not telling you!"

"You had another nightdress."

"My skin I'm not willing to sell!"

"Did you buy it, then?"

"I stole it. There's plenty growing on the Pincian Hill as it is!"

"You're a genius, and I love you!" I say, and I serve myself a huge portion of the forbidden vegetable.

Saint Augustine was haunted by guilt his entire life because in his youth he stole a pear. We, on the other hand, have fallen so low in our morals that the mere fact that the cabbage is stolen seems to replace the zest of the bacon we'd like to have cooked it with.

But maybe you can't really call it theft, Diana going for a walk in the park on the Pincian Hill to the little cluster of forgotten cabbages growing around the slightly antiquated sign that says "Victory will be ours!" After all, the Duce did plant them so that the citizens of Rome should be able the more effectively to resist the enemy. We are Romans, and our enemy is hunger!

If Mussolini added a sad chapter to the history of Italy, which the levelled Renaissance palaces of Rome can be called to witness, it will be recalled here, where everything flows into everything else (historically), up on the Pincian Hill. The tour guides of the distant future will explain it to the visitors of the day: "Ladies and Gentlemen, on this hill lay Sallust's incredible gardens – he bled Africa white so that Rome could have the richest gardens in the world! In the middle ages, this was where they buried women of ill-repute, with marble tombs of no less repute, where cardinals would send wreaths of rare blooms on All Souls. This is where Napoleon's landscape artist, Valadier, built his lovely ascent, and this is where Benito Mussolini ordered the cabbages to grow!"

The affair with the cabbages started because in 1941 and 1942 Rome was the most peaceful of the capitals of the fighting powers, so much so that Mussolini's war seemingly neither affected nor interested it at all. The Duce wanted to see determined, dour-faced Prussians on the *Via Veneto* in place of the elegant ladies and gentlemen promenading in the sunshine, but since he could not import the foggy mornings of Hamburg, by mid-afternoon the cafes were full of people drinking bad coffee and sweet marsala wine, eating ice-cream and talking about football and the pictures, while offensively elegant women discussed the eternally mysterious things (entirely unconnected with war) that offensively elegant women do discuss, by turns laughing or whispering, depending on their current topic. It was very hard to do anything about them, especially since a good part of the well-dressed young men were party functionaries, and the elegant ladies their wives and mistresses. Besides, any industry of any importance at all ceased by four, if not two, in the afternoon. In some places, above all the ministries, the work done even before then was of a purely symbolic nature. There was a war on, the factories should have been going full-blast day and night, but even though there aren't that many factories in Rome, there wasn't enough fuel for the few that there were, and they functioned two or three days a week at most. It was the same as in peacetime – poverty was swept under the carpet, luxury promenaded itself. Even the strikingly elegant officers and the generals with their gold and silver medals served merely to heighten the carefree, glittering atmosphere. Also, it was hard to order people to wear serious faces when day after day they were officially reassured that "all was well in this best of all possible worlds", that "England is starving", that "tomorrow, we'll reach Moscow", "the Japanese are winning the war", "the Americans are drunken half-bloods", and that "Germany is strong."

It should have been the party's job to create this Spartan atmosphere, and so the primary responsibility for the planting of the cabbages fell to Achille Starace, the party secretary. He was the one who prescribed a new way of life to go with the new political system. The fascists thought of everything and the party's official organ announced that it was forbidden to perform the Roman salute while sitting, and that you weren't allowed to wear a top hat with your black shirt. When one day they banned restaurants from seating more than four people at one table, lest in these serious times someone should be seen to be making merry, his influence could be suspected. The result was that families with several children had to order a side-table to go with their soup. Achille survived the fall of countless ministers in office. Mussolini was different to Hitler in that two or three times a year he would sack all his ministers under the guise of a "changing of the guard" (or, as was more popularly said, "new donkeys for the trough"), while Hitler kept his Göring and his Goebbels. Hitler, with his persecution mania, was afraid of new faces, while Mussolini was an actor, ever in need of a change of audience. But Achille stayed on as party secretary. "Mussolini always changes his ministers for even stupider ones", people said in Rome, "but there's none to be found dumber than Achille". They say he even ordered uniforms for his secret bodyguard. He was also the one who personally showed us how to save petrol – one day, dressed top to toe in white – he would cycle to work, the next, he'd drive in in a pony trap and civilian garb, while the third, he'd ride into work on a pony in a militia leader's uniform. In fact, he sometimes even walked, but when he did, he took some photographers with him to record the event ("even the party secretary walks to work").

But just so there's no historical confusion, and perhaps for our own benefit so that we should know who to be grateful to for our cabbage and meal, it was the Duce, or so the radio announced one day, who had decided that every scrap of space must be put to use and had ordered the city parks to be planted with cabbage stew. Not much later, the photographs appeared, showing the Emperor Augustus' bronze statue standing on the *Via dell'Imperio*, surrounded by cabbages. Julius Caesar contemplated the Colosseum covered in cauliflowers. Thoughtful types even made little signs with "war garden" and "we're winning!" emblazoned on them. The Duce's toppling and then the city's fall deprived the little plantations of their guards, and so thanks to Diana's daring raid, the victory cabbages united their efforts with our reserves of meal.

We hadn't had the chance yet to scoop out the thick paste at the bottom of our plates when Eckstein knocked. He had carefully picked the correct moment.

"The situation?" I ask.

Eckstein is prepared for the question, and answers well, as befitting a writer.

"After the Lateran Accords, the papers said that Mussolini had given Italy to God, and God to Italy. Now Hitler has given Italy to Mussolini, and Mussolini to the Italians."

"Just so," Diana confirms, and asks her rhetorical question – "Would you like some cabbage and meal?"

Looking for a nice turn of phrase myself, I repeat Diana's question, and add – "as long as you don't mind that it grew out of the ashes of Renaissance ladies of the night!"

"Hush!"

Diana's angry, but Eckstein is too busy trying to break down the hunger-wall between him and reality. Extrapolating from my previous thought to the present day, I ask, "What does Ariane say?"

I don't hurry Eckstein to respond, because I know that a discussion of the way things stand belongs firmly in the post-prandial world. Eckstein replies only after his third spoonful.

"The colonel went into hiding yesterday afternoon, and not a soul will be able to find him."

"In a monastery?"

"No, in his wife's flat."

"In other words, the general won."

"Modern technology has equipped generals with a special mechanism which ensures that they automatically disappear at critical junctures. Before he did disappear, though, the general told a nice little story, which he was now at liberty to tell, seeing that the king's disappeared too (also being a general). On the twenty-fifth of July, after the decision of the Grand Council, Mussolini went up to see the king one last time. He wanted to explain to him that just because the fascist top brass had lost confidence in him, that didn't mean that he had to resign. The king didn't reply, but instead sang him, in Piedmontese dialect, the song the soldiers sing, the one that tells him to go and…"

"More cabbage?" Diana asks.

"I'm talking about history here. I can just imagine the little old man, singing in his nasal voice, his grey moustache twitching away. And I can imagine Mussolini, who until then had only had the *Giovinezzia* sung in his honour, listening to the king's little ditty. *Ecco*: that's Italy for you. The home of opera. What an aria and what a finale! Cadence and curtain. The king hums the tune, the people applaud. And while the king was still singing, the ambulance was already there in the garden, waiting to take his audience away. A proper, Red Cross ambulance, too, the only difference being that instead of paramedics, it was stuffed with *carabinieri*. Just to be on the safe side, they brought a strait jacket too. This might have been the Duce's last disguise. But he was so awed by the song that he went to the ambulance without resisting."

"Is that really true?" Diana asks. "After all, it was the general who promised us paratroopers, too!"

"No, that was the colonel. Either way, I believe it. The Mussolini affair began and ended like a *da capo* aria. The scene is in every schoolboy's textbook: after the March on Rome, the Duce goes up to the king and says 'I present you with the Italy of the *Vittorio Veneto!*' Keep that image in mind, and put that other one next to it. Twenty years later, the same Duce, the same king – the king singing while the Duce listens morosely, and in the background, a captain waits with a strait jacket slung over his arm."

"And yet he's back in power!"

"*Momento!* I wouldn't be too sure about that. Hitler's made a grand little speech, although of course these days he's a little more cautious, since the BBC's been playing his *Stalingrad berennen und es auch nehmen werdent – we will overrun and capture Stalignrad* every single day, but we still don't know what he's going to send Mussolini back here to do."

"Oh, I believe in the solidarity of kings and dictators, but above all in the solidarity of tyrants!"

"It's not in Germany's interests to make an Italian government. It has no arms to give, and wouldn't want to give them to the Italians anyway, since they've been trying to take the ones they *do* have away from them. They know full well that the country is not fascist. In any case, they're probably bored of their little ally who's constantly asking for things. What should they bother with him for? Wouldn't it be easier to send a German general to be regent instead?"

Diana and I both look at the empty cabbage-pot and I'm sure we're both thinking the exact same thing – "we still have the cheese, there's hope yet!"

"One possible solution would be to make a second Vichy in some south-Tyrolean village," Eckstein ponders.

"Yes, I'm sure Mussolini would like that. After all, Pétain is not a bad role-model. The Germans like him, because he's a well-behaved collaborationist, and also because tyrants like to shake the hands of chiefs of staff, be it Pétain or Hindenburg, just as long as they weren't the ones to install them... He's good for the French because the British don't really bomb them much and are promising to liberate them, and the Germans daren't really hurt them... Mussolini's played so many roles already that he could play Pétain's in his sleep!"

"Just as Badoglio would play it for the British."

I can't resist sharing one of my night terrors with my friend, especially since I think him optimist enough to contradict me. "What if Hitler makes a separate peace? Mussolini will be begging him to send his entire army of the East down here!"

Eckstein doesn't disappoint – he contradicts me at once. "Out of the question. And I'll tell you why: it's a question of psychology. I've given this question some thought, and I know that it's an easy one." He takes another long look into the cabbage-pot, and then continues as if he were pondering the Thirty Years' War.

"This second war is the worst of the outcomes of the first. For the Germans, it's something else, too, it's the new and improved version. In that, Hitler and the *Volk* are perfectly agreed. For twenty years, the central theme of every German book about the war was "what was it that lost us the war?" Ludendorff's answer was because they didn't occupy Arras. Hitler occupied it. Hindenburg though that Reims was where it all turned sour. Hitler occupied it. The admirals said they should have had a thousand submarines and big naval battles should have been out of the question. Hitler gave them their thousand submarines. Some people said it was Italy's intervention that decided the war. This time around, therefore, poor Italy became a German ally. But no-one said that concluding a separate peace with Russia helped Germany's situation, and that's why there won't be another Brest-Litovsk. Not to mention the fact that the Russians would never go for it."

"The Allies will be here in two weeks!" Diana chimes in with the chorus.

Eckstein carefully balances his disagreement with optimism:

"Serious, positive events might delay this relatively minor (but from our point of view, happy) occasion. For example, a Balkan landing. After all, the Allies have already achieved their goal here, which was to knock Italy out of the war. They certainly don't need the territory; whether Germany extends to Naples or Bologna doesn't matter a jot to them, only to us. Landing at Saloniki on the other hand, and making it up to the Romanian oil fields…"

"I want the Eighth Army to liberate Rome!" Diana insists obstinately.

"And they will. Their problem is that they hardly have room on the beach at Salerno to unpack all that gear they brought with them. It's slow going and hard till Naples. Once they take Naples, though, it really will be only fourteen days!"

"We should listen once and see what the German radio is saying."

"I heard it yesterday. It didn't say anything at all. It talked about Russia, and Fortress Europe and some new kind of submarine."

"Nothing about Italy? Even the British hardly said a word about Rome."

Eckstein once more speaks as if we were mere onlookers to this diabolical comedy and not extras in it.

"The fact is, no-one likes the way things stand."

"Me neither," Diana says honestly.

"For Hitler, the Italian armistice is psychologically a second Stalingrad. He lost the thing that's most important to a paranoiac – the illusion that everyone's singing his tune. It turns out that the young, Northern, Aryan Italians, the guardians of the New Order are not so young, but old and wise and don't give two hoots about his ideology. Forty million Julian Apostates! Or what's worse, a thousand anti-German generals. But the worst part is that it turns out that the Duce, once you put him in jail, is nothing more than a pathetic cry-baby! It's enough to make you weep. There's a reassuring term now for battles you lose: 'a retreat to prepared positions'. Or, 'we adopted a hedgehog formation', and so forth. There's no such comforting term for political disaster, unless they start saying that their enemies are few and everyone adores the *Führer*. Goebbels can make the defeat at Stalingrad sound like the last chapter in the *Nibelungslied,* but there's no denying and no dressing up the fact that someone – pardon my French – crapped on a statue of Mussolini on the main street in broad daylight! But the British don't like this week's events, either. Italy is out of the war, but not quite. The question is still what's better? A weak enemy or a weak ally? Italy has proved to be a very weak ally indeed. The German troops are still exactly where they were last week. In other words, no-one likes the way things stand."

I reflect that Ariane can't be pleased, either, what with the officer corps disappearing overnight, and the officers themselves can hardly be pleased with their new civilian clothes, and the colonel's wife certainly can't be pleased that he's chosen to hide in her flat, of all places. Not even Mussolini can be pleased that he has to go through Munich on his way home, with the memories of Churchill and Daladier nodding along sagely to his words. Maybe only the *Tramontana* is pleased to have been able to rage freely through the land of Latium, but even the wind has got tired now, and slunk off somewhere.

Our friend, too, starts to gather his things to go. It would be a shame to ruin his parting with more words, so I turn to the piano. I wonder, though, whether there's a composer in Europe today who could convey the mood of our present reality in music, who could encapsulate our day-to-day lives in a symphony? Does he exist, a latter-day Respighi, who could compose his modern chords about the pine-trees in Rome and the crickets that sit in them, about the city's fountains and the children who play around them? How could one play – I have no idea, as my fingers search for the keys – the tanks trundling along the endless Russian plain, anxious to secure the wheat before the onset of winter? That melody should include the tune of "Lili Marlene", the only German song in this war that is fundamentally nostalgic not about the war, but about peace and freedom, the poor, tinkling peace of the organ-grinders, just as Schumann incorporates the "Marsellaise" at the end of the "beiden Grenadiere". All at once, my hands move randomly around the keyboard – it shouldn't be music at all, but a Punch and Judy show, one they can put on for children on the Pincian Hill. The Black Duke would come, sing his Cabbage Aria, and beat the table with his fists. Up would pop the Compact King, hum his little soldier's tune and then whack the Black Duke over the head. The Duke vanishes. The Compact King summons the Ancient General – they drink and dance. Then, all of sudden, the Black Duke appears from the wings with a crocodile and the King and the

General vanish. The Duke and the crocodile face the audience and lift their right paws in salute.

"What on earth is that racket?" Diana asks. "*Mio caro*, are you all right?"

"Sorry," I mutter, not daring to admit that I was in fact working on a contemporary opera. "You're absolutely right. Pass me the second volume of the *Wohltemperiertes*. I'll play you the twelfth prelude!" I know that Diana forgives me many things when I play it. The procession of preludes and fugues move with ancient dignity through this unwelcome day. I feel and know that the only things that remain pure are the ones the war can't touch. The fleeting, transitory play of sounds is something that's eternal and pure. It shows that there's still some order somewhere, although don't ask me where – in the realm of wavelengths, between the covers of the score, or in our little room in the wake of my fingers. The important thing is, it exists. Perhaps Nostradamus could predict the events of the future in the same way as Bach predicted what I would be playing today. There are forces that determine the future, empires that last a thousand years – you just have to dream them properly.

In the evenings, the ordered row of thoughts turns back upon itself and retraces its steps. In their slowing merry-go-round, images and words are repeated, while dreams fly out in straight lines. In the morning, it's the tired dreams that start their circling, just as the homing pigeon coming home circles its roost, and the dream-images repeat themselves, ever more faded as they do. The poet will find rhyme and rhythm most easily in this pell-mell whirlpool between consciousness and sleep, and if he can keep himself awake at night or not quite wake up in the morning and stay on the very threshold of consciousness, he might dream a poem whose birth neither his conscious self, nor the literary critic, nor even the omniscient psychologist can explain. We mortals flee our prosaic lives a moment more in the sweet unconsciousness of morning, and after all why not? Why not flee when the world around us is a mad dictator's dream, made real? But then hunger, thirst, and light, the powers that wake even the sleeping infant, will rouse us to consciousness.

Hunger comes from within, the light comes through the walls of our little glass house; and I am forced to admit that it is once again morning. I have to find bread, and find out how things stand – where the wind has blown the little ship of our destiny while we slept.

Diana is having breakfast in her sleep. When she does, she passes from Renaissance goddess to Baroque, but she is ever as angelically young. With her cheeks slightly puffed, like the air bags on an organ, and locks of her hair falling onto her forehead, she's savouring the few minutes that she can steal from cruel day's account and transfer to comforting slumber.

I go out to get bread, news, and water. I get the news first.

"Those shits took their weapons!" I hear on the fifth floor.

"They arrested those little shits!" the second floor window announces.

My reader would be forgiven for thinking that the news refers to some crime, and its punishment, but standing in line at the bakery – or rather I should say, wading through the crowd – waiting for the poor yellow cornbread that the Romans call "egg bread", I learn the correct interpretation of the word "shits" in today's bulletin. On the fifth floor, it means "the German paratroopers", and on the second it means "the unfortunate Piave Division".

Mussolini got out, Badoglio disappeared, the dictatorship is back, and one would expect there to be the sort of silence at the bakery that usually governs groups of people in such situations, unless they've had specific orders to scream and shout. But of silence there is none. The *jus murmurandi* has, for forty-five days, been *jus clamandi*, and the image of the bogeyman has not yet scared into silence those who only recently were tearing their mouths with new and unaccustomed self-expression. And besides, we're in the artists' quarter and not near the ministries, surrounded by functionaries! The functionary, as the Italians are fond of saying – will hitch his donkey wherever he's told. What's more, he'll take care to see that others also do the same, and don't espouse different views from his master on how donkeys ought to be hitched. He is able to present the donkey-hitching instructions of the day as if they sprang from his innermost soul. He is perfectly capable of having someone arrested or denounced if they dare to present revolutionary – seditious – views on stabling or straw.

Our baker – a good and decent man who was inside for a year for giving some people more bread than the donkey-hitchers would have liked – has the right sort of clientele. The people of the *vie Laurina, Gesú e Maria, Fontanella Borghese,* and *Margutta* are, *per Bacco* (by Bacchus!), good people I swear. Can one judge people by what street they live in? I say you can – at least, you can in Rome. I know there are other criteria by which one can group one's fellow human beings – psychologists divide people into introverts and extroverts, students of the soul and the body into Don Quixotes and Sancho Panzas, experts on the neurology of the body into vagotonic and sympathicotonic. The Pope would probably prefer their division into the sinful masses and the small minority leading holy lives (which principle serves to exclude democracy, the rule of the masses, from the Church). The official German view, which extends from Narvik to the Sorrento peninsula, divides humanity into a Northern, Aryan group (to which the Japanese belong in spirit) and a trash-heap (in which only the Arabs stand out), and maintains that history is made up of the clash between the two, and that after the *Götterdämmerung* shaking heaven and earth today, the former will triumph over the evil domination of the latter. According to this philosophy, the residents of Baboon, Laurina, Jesus and Mary, and Borghese Fountain Street should be waging war on the rag-pickers and artichoke boilers who live behind the *Campo de'Fiori.*

Conveniently, though, this philosophy is false. Humanity cannot be divided into two groups – black and white, devils and angels – and I'm afraid that at the Final Judgement it might be hard to sort who belongs in heaven and who in hell. No, groups of people are made up differently. In Italy, there's no doubt – the core of the community is your immediate family, which presents a unified face to the world while waging its own internal struggles. This is the primary, strong citadel of the individual, into which he can retreat from the cruel world. The second circle (and it seems perfectly natural that Dante should divide his hell into circles) is the *tribú*, the Latin *tribús*, or group of families, which looks up, back to the grandfather (really the grandmother, though). This is an almost state-like system of kinship, which maintains close or inimical diplomatic relations with other *tribús*; the members of a *tribú* may belong to the same party, work at the same ministry, and their star rise and fall with the ascent and downfall of their leader. It was only the *tribús* of the fascist grandees who were sorry about the events of the twenty-fifth of July. The next circle out is the circle of your neighbourhood, where you live, the centuries-old secret Roman society of the residents of various unchanging constellations of streets.

Often in Italy, the separate – to the outsider, indistinguishable – groups of streets have their own, very different, spirits. The handful of Sienese *contrada*s, or districts, compete with each other not only on the day of the *Palio*, but throughout the year. In Assisi, the peaceful, sleepy home of Saint Francis, the upper and lower towns have been cohabiting in an unpleasant state of tension for the last seven hundred years. The streets of Naples each celebrate different Saint's days, and Rome – not the Rome of the modern apartment buildings, villas, factories and ministries, but the old, sacred Rome – is divided into a huge number of little villages. Unlike the fierce Tuscans, they live well together side by side, all the more because their inhabitants have built invisible screens around their neighbourhoods and do not venture out of theirs and into others'. The men sometimes – reluctantly and with a certain sadness – go off to hunt (for food, or money), but the women guard the hearth, and talk about the neighbouring district as if it were the other side of the world. Near the *Piazza Navona*, in the Street of Baboons, there are old ladies who were born here, and who have yet to see St Peter's square.

These little principalities (and wasn't Italy so much better off when it was made up of little principalities?) are more or less independent. In ours, we have a baker (though these days he may be out of bread), a milkman (even though his milk is now *ersatz*), and a grocer (nowadays selling grass dressed as

234

salad). Our little principality's wealth is ensured by our traditional industries (although sculpture and painting are traditional industries too, they don't necessarily generate wealth) – our two houses of ill repute, one of which is reputable, and the other less so. The little world of us breadwinners who line up in the morning at the bakery to discuss the latest events and deposit the life-giving half loaf in our baskets or coat pockets, blends perfectly well with these established and traditional institutions that elsewhere are considered dens of vice. The hairdresser's livelihood is doing the young ladies' hair, the laundry is busy washing their linen – and there's plenty to wash – the milkman sends them the very last of his black concoction to contain any real coffee, and the coalman gives them their special rations, because it's not only the residents of the *Laurino* who respect these institutions, but also the state (because they pay a lot of taxes).

Our little principality looks upon the doors of these almsgiving institutions with honest respect, and no hypocrisy. The Street of Baboons was paved from their taxes, when the Papal state turned their tax income to the public good. And where should a good mother send a twenty-year old son suffering agonies because he's not yet married, but has nonetheless become a man? Where should the husbands go if their imagination has given up the ghost after twenty greying years? And how should a poor girl keep her child if she can't come and spend a couple of weeks now and then in the house on the *via Laurina*?

The sculptor who's spent the last twenty years depicting the heroic blackshirts rushing from one side of the composition to the other is now ashamed, and removes the plaque from his door – the houses in the *via Laurina* have no such problem displaying the chains on their shutters.

My practice extends only as far as the frontiers of this little principality. Once I treated a man for lumbago on the other side of the *Corso*, deep in foreign territory. But I know every courtyard of my three streets; in fact, the upstanding and respectable proprietress of the laundry introduced me to the madame of the less respectable of the two bawdy houses in the *Via Laurina*, who was complaining of varicose veins. She received me up in the roof garden, and while we chatted about her legs, I was watching the barefoot young Augustinian monks playing football on their own roof, not so very far away on my right. The ball could easily have come over the little gap separating the very different worlds of the two roofs.

I'm at home here in this little principality whose frontiers I crossed without a passport, and I know that I can speak freely in the little crowd of my fellow-citizens clamouring for bread. Italy may be living under a dictatorship, but in the section of the Street of Baboons stretching from the Jesus and Mary church to the more reputable of the houses of ill-repute, freedom of speech lives on.

I've gotten hold of the two longish loaves of *sfilatini*, with their time-honoured shape. If they were white and sweet-smelling, like they used to be, I would probably tear into them at once and stuff my mouth with them, apologising abjectly to Diana afterwards (who, being not only a goddess but an angel too, would forgive me). As it is, the temptation is not so irresistible, and I might even walk down to the corner of the *Piazza del Popolo* on my way back, so as not to arrive early and wake Diana too soon. From the corner, I look back down the pretty street, straight as an arrow, swept clean by yesterday's wind, and I imagine the liberating British troops marching down it. Leading them will be the dour Scottish pipers, the ecstatic populace lining the street either side – the bohemians of the *Via Margutta*, us, the girls of the *Via Laurina*, the baker...

I've got an idea! And I'm going to make it happen. A hundred thousand people in the streets, all wanting to talk to the liberators. They'll need a little phrasebook, with the most useful everyday expressions. I'm going to write it, find someone to publish it, and sell a hundred thousand copies the day we get liberated. Or perhaps it'll only be fifty thousand, but even so, if I get just one lira per copy, we'll be set! The first thing I'll buy Diana is three nightgowns, and I'll have a stove put in our studio, so that we won't have to freeze, like we did last winter.... or I'll sell the idea to a publisher right now for two bottles of oil. This bread is lousy, but if we could fry it in oil, it would make a meal fit for a king! Actually, I'll settle for just a single bottle of oil, too.

Diana must still be sleeping, so I take a turn around the piazza, it helps me think. The peripatetic thinkers were right, the rhythm of one's steps leads one's thoughts.

I'm going to write a little phrasebook. Standard conversations are all so similar, it won't be hard to predict them. People talk when they meet, just as ants touch feelers, without necessarily having anything to communicate. I'm going to think of some little dialogues... actually, the idea is not a new one. I remember the BBC talking about a book like this the British had found in the pockets of a German pilot they'd shot down. "Brush up your English while you bomb!" said the mellifluous voice of the presenter. "We know that the enemy think methodically, and make use of every spare moment. We don't need to spend our time reading English phrasebooks, since we're familiar with our own language. Nonetheless, it will perhaps be instructive to learn it anew from this little book..." he continued, and then read out some of the most striking phrases. "Are you carrying any concealed weapons?", "Hand it over, or you will be shot". "Ju vil bi shott", the announcer spelled out for us, "Where is the money?"... "Whoever doesn't accept occupation Marks...vil bi shott". The BBC did nothing more than quote from the little book, and express its surprise that there was also a conversation entitled "At Tea" ("Yes, I would like another piece of pie"), and that the introduction claimed that the aim of the little booklet was the furthering of good relations between the populace and the occupying forces.

Might Diana be awake already? I head home. My book will be different – I'm simply going to translate the things we will say to our liberators. "It's good that you're here!", "At last, finally". "Why couldn't you have landed on September the eighth, already?" "Where were the paratroopers?" and "Do you happen to have a tin of corned beef?". "Don't go on! What for? The war is over. What, the Germans are still messing around up there? So what? Let them!" but no, I can't say that – I have to say "Go, liberate the Nazis' prisoners, save those that can still be saved!". "We were very hungry". "I'll sell my radio, I don't care anymore what happens, I want some milk".

I head home to present the full plan to Diana. "Darling, while you were sleeping, I had a terrific idea. Our worries are over. We'll write the dialogues for Rome's happiest day. I even have the title: "Talking to Tommies". Everyone will get it!" (Mussolini wrote a little book called "Conversations with Bruno". His son, Bruno, was a pilot, but he'd never even had a whiff of action, he was larking around on an airfield near Livorno somewhere. In the afternoons he'd do a circuit or two over their villa, for his wife's amusement. One afternoon, he crashed, and so it was to him that his father addressed his morose, patriotic thoughts. The book was not printed for "popular distribution", but they printed countless copies for charity and every functionary, party member, and merchant could order one, or put another way, was in trouble if he didn't. The Italians respect the concept of piety, even if the father was an uninteresting dictator, the son a shiftless officer, and didn't mess around about buying it. They did not, however, read the blessed thing, but merely quoted its title in conversation). That's why mine will be an even more effective title!

The *Piazza del Popolo* is already warm from the autumn sun. The only shade in its circular vastness is the thin sliver cast by the obelisk in the middle. Once, in the library, I came across a funny little book from the last century: "Roman city-walks in the shade". It had been written by a priest, and related in detail where the shade was in the mornings and in the afternoons, where one could take a brief respite in the coolness of one of the grand *palazzi*. But he was stumped by this square. *Qui si salta - let's skip over this square*, he wrote. Now, the warm sunshine feeds me instead of breakfast. I go round the square once more.

Yes, the Germans had their book of conversational English. The Germans have minutely prepared the finest details of our current catastrophes. The Germans always think of everything, except the truly critical things, which make them lose wars. The British, on the other hand, think only of victory, and will be perfectly capable of marching into Berlin without

238

little books of conversational German. But before all that, they'll march in here – in fourteen days.

And that will be my chance to go down in history. I'm going to go straight to the publishers; maybe one of them will take my little stroke of genius on.

The publishers… Diana sold her pearls, her set of Proust, and then finally her nightgowns. I have only myself to sell. Not in the same way as Ariane, of course – besides, Ariane doesn't sell herself either, maybe a smile or two here and there, but never her innermost thoughts. I, on the other hand, will sell my thoughts, my time, my soul, if I can find a publisher. I would rather sell my soul to the devil, who would even lease it back to me for the duration of my life on earth, if he would offer me three bottles of olive oil. But Beelzebub is spoilt for choice these days, and his cup runneth over so, that he hasn't time to be bothered with me. I'll have to make do with the publishers. I'll go and see the manager of the publishers who do the Encyclopaedia – a little man who had a vast armchair installed in his office, and spends all his time standing in front of that. If you don't know him, you think he's sitting down, and doesn't seem so small. His secretary is a retired Major. He stands behind his desk like a little pig-faced bigshot and screams "Major!" in the tone of voice that generals alone use. I know what he's going to say to me: "I can pay you the ministry's official rate". This rate is a little souvenir of the good old days before the war. The ministry that published it has ceased to exist, but the rate itself lives on. Or I could offer my "Tommy" (I already think of it as a finished work) to the Imperial Publishers, to the man with the limp who's so deeply unpopular with the ladies of the typing pool. Or maybe I could offer it to Narcissus Publishing, where there are no ladies in the typing pool, only ladylike young men, who are deeply unpopular with me… oh well. All publishers are alike. Paper is equally attractive to bohemian souls who like to write and have no real idea about money, and those who are aware that money is printed on paper. The publisher is convinced that writers are trying to take advantage of him. They buy a piece of paper for ten lira, write the translation of some popular novel or other, or the E to F section of a medical dictionary on it, and then offer this same piece of paper to him for a thousand lira. His self-respect demands that he haggle the price down a bit, pay late, and if at all possible with an unsecured cheque. Perhaps there are publishers who are different – I once read a book on logic that said that you shouldn't try and predict the future on the basis of a series of similar past events. Over the course of several tens of centuries, people observed that swans were white, and therefore expected the swans of tomorrow to be the same. Then one fine day they landed in Australia and found the black swan that logically should not have existed. It's the hope of finding my own black swan that drives me from poorly-paying patients to poorly-paying publishers.

It's true, though, that it's partly my fault, for going back again and again to the leeches who feed me. I like paper, the smell of printer's ink, and books as yet unborn. I can't write books – hunger releases me for so short a time after lunch, and even that little time is not mine, because when I'm full, I fall straight into the arms of sleep, who lets me go only when it's time to hand me over to hunger again. I also can't write because I've taken on too big a task – writing the history of European cuisine – and am therefore seizing every excuse to work on something a little smaller. I'd rather translate, squandering the little time I have, in the knowledge, as the words flow from Norwegian into Italian, that in all reality, I'm just shirking my true task. At last, I can take a book between my hands, my name is on the cover; but it's not really my book, I was just the dictionary for it. I avoided the terror of the blank page. I take on all sorts of pernickety little jobs, and envy the slaves in the ancient copying-houses, who got to read the great, lost works, knew Petronius' full *oeuvre*, and could enjoy the elegant classical Greek recipes of the *Deipnosophistae*. At the same time, I envy my communist friends who are convinced that soon, a new state will come and save them, have done with publishers, and replace them with an honest clerk who will purchase the writers' work with a supportive gesture, and repay them with the opportunity to relax and to create. I personally hope for nothing more from my new idea than getting through, by hook or by crook, those fourteen days' worth of meals until our deliverance.

Diana is decorating her hair with her old hairbrush and a handful of fresh sunshine.

"Darling, I've got it!" I say, and explain to her my idea about "Tommy". "We'll write a book! You can write the Italian bits, and I'll do the English. The first dialogue can be "The Weather". It's fine today, shame about the weather, yesterday was better, tomorrow will be nicer... then what should be next?"

"I don't know, I don't know the English."

"Come on, what will people talk about when they talk to an English colonel, say?"

Diana pauses for with the brush for no more than a second.

"'Dialogue with an English Colonel': I love you, I need you, take me to Hollywood!"

"Diana, please!"

"Well, you asked!"

"The Allied army..."

"Exists somewhere, yes. But when they come here, they won't be an army any more, but two hundred thousand well-fed, healthy, good-looking boys, English, French and American."

I don't know quite what my expression betrays, but Diana continues in a tone of consolation:

"The Fifth army, the Eighth army, that's one reality. You yourself said that different realities can co-exist in the same time and place... and the two hundred thousand boys is another reality. The Germans came. That's an army. When the British come, they'll be just people, people you can talk to. Don't you see?"

"But we're waiting for them to come and liberate us!"

"That's one reality, yes. But Ariane, for example..."

"Her too!"

"She's not waiting for the Allies, I talked to her, I know. She's waiting for a general."

"Who? Eisenhower? Clark?"

"Don't be silly. Just a general; what his name is, is completely beside the point. You can't write dialogues for people waiting to be liberated. You can't chit-chat with Liberation."

I can feel that Diana has won.

241

Printed in Hungary